THE WORLD
OF SMALL ANIMALS

The World of Small Animals

Theodore H. Savory

M.A., F.Z.S.

UNIVERSITY OF LONDON PRESS LTD.
WARWICK SQUARE, LONDON, E.C.4

Printed & Bound in England for the UNIVERSITY OF LONDON PRESS, LTD.,
by HAZELL, WATSON & VINEY, LTD., Aylesbury and London

Preface

THIS book is an elaboration of a doctrine that I have preached for years to all the natural historians I have known. Its simple text is that they will get most enjoyment and the most worth-while results from their natural history if they adopt as their own one of the less popular orders or families of small invertebrates.

It is easy to convince a young naturalist whose interest in living things has already been aroused that he would be wise to try the suggestion; it is much harder for the boy himself to make a start, because there is very little information to help him in the earlier stages. The consequence is that, although he realises the attractiveness of becoming a "specialist," he may find it too difficult to convert himself into one.

I have tried here to supply him with a guide through the early obstacles. I have assumed almost no knowledge of biology or of the methods of professional zoologists, either in the field or the laboratory, or in describing or naming the animals on which they are working; but have tried first to explain, in general terms, the activities of a student of small animals, and have then offered short introductory surveys of a number of suitable groups to which, among many others, my thesis of amateur-specialisation can be applied.

I have been tempted to make the experiment of writing this book by the increasing interest in all forms of natural history which has been so definite a feature of the last few years. This has been in conspicuous contrast with the years between the two Great Wars, when for a time even butterflies and birds commanded fewer devotees than of old: it is probably due in part to the spread of biology teaching among schools of all kinds; in part to the wholly admirable influence in this direction of the B.B.C.; and in part to the fact that a highly taxed people is to some extent compelled to seek its recreation in simpler, less expensive and more satisfying pleasures. Among such pleasures natural history occupies a very high place, and the hope behind the writing of this book is that it may help the interested beginner to develop into the serious student and to convert the amateur naturalist into the zoologist who is capable of making—who is in fact certain to make—real contributions to Science.

In trying to do this I have been forced to compress my own speciality, the Arachnida, into fewer pages than my prejudice would lead me to give them, and to write many pages about small animals of which from personal labours I know but a little, and more about others of which I know even less. For my temerity in doing this I must beg the indulgence of those who know springtails and woodlice and centipedes more intimately than I, and ask them to admit that the purpose of my writing at all was my justification for thus trespassing in their fields.

Finally, I wish to thank a number of boys of Haberdashers' Aske's Hampstead School, especially C. I. Carter, T. J. Pryke, and J. K. Sholl, who have supplied me with many specimens of animals mentioned in the following pages, and so have helped me to see something of the things I have described! And I owe a special word of gratitude to Miss H. J. Vanderplank, who has drawn the illustrations.

T. H. S.

Acknowledgments

The author and publishers make grateful acknowledgment to Messrs. Michael Joseph Ltd. for permission to quote an extract from *The Happy Prisoner*, by Monica Dickens; and to the following firms and individuals for the use of photographs in this book:

Mondiale Literary Services, Paul Popper, Lynwood M. Chace, Hugh Spencer, John Ward, Richard L. Cassell, Charles E. Mettler, Eric Hudson, Robert C. Hermes, W. W. Roberts, John Markham, and the Natural History Museum, South Kensington.

Contents

PART ONE
Small Animals

PART TWO

8 *Contents*

List of Plates

PART ONE

Chapter I

SMALL ANIMALS: THEIR POSSIBILITIES

TIMES change, and nowadays change more rapidly, it seems, than in the past. Natural History, as it used to be pursued in the unbelievably distant days before the First World War, is dead; or, if not dead, is changed out of all recognition. It was a pleasant pastime, sociable, with sufficient intrinsic value to justify itself as a hobby, and not too intellectual. It gave to its devotees an added enjoyment in a countryside which they accepted as a normal inheritance and which is now vanishing before their eyes under dormitory-towns, arterial roads and aerodromes; and it provided an excuse for rambles or forays afoot and for excursions or expeditions on bicycles which, though they may have laid undue emphasis on a picnic tea, were thoroughly enjoyable and very well worth while. But the spirit of those quiet days has flown, taking wings before the applications of physical science, and one undoubted consequence of the First War was that man suffered the loss of the chief factor of contentment, the ability to appreciate simple pleasures.

In the years following 1918, this fact was in many ways evident; and in few was it more pronounced than in the indifference with which the wild life of the fields was generally regarded. A wise man could regret these evolutionary changes, but he might also see them as evanescent: he could regard them with interest, or even with a certain pride that he had lived in the most remarkable generation the world had known. He would be assured that if Natural History was really as valuable as had been thought, then it would surely survive, even if in a modified form. And this has, indeed, happened.

In its earlier form, Natural History was dominated by collectors. We all collected—that is, we caught, killed, named, labelled and preserved: and now it is universally recognised how unintelligent a process this was, and how little removed from the wholesale gathering of wild flowers that we resent in the thoughtless and vulgar. It was no more than an easy sublimation of the acquisitive complex, and not more than one collection in a hundred was ever able to serve any other purpose, even to its owner.

This element has disappeared. Natural History has tried, with some success, to teach the creed of the ecologist; and now it is observation and experiment that are praised, rather than acquisition or piracy. Biology is the study of living things, not the alignment of empty egg-shells and desiccated insects; the egg-collector has become the bird-watcher, and through the new Natural History there comes a better understanding of the phenomena of Biology and a truer appreciation of the problems that it offers for solution.

It is the purpose of this chapter to describe, and the purpose of the rest of this book to facilitate, the course which should, in the writer's opinion and experience, be taken as an alternative to intensive acquisition or the even more deplorable fading of early enthusiasm.

A young naturalist who begins, as most of us do begin, with the study of butterflies or birds or beetles, finds that he is dealing with a group of animals of which the known British species are numbered by scores or even by hundreds or thousands. He is, moreover, one of dozens or scores of biologists who are similarly occupied, and who are working with material that has already been well investigated for a century or more. He therefore finds that unless he has unusual facilities for travel his collection is not likely to represent, at least for some years, more than a small fraction of the known British fauna. He will find plenty of available information to help him to learn what others have already discovered about the animals of his choice, but he will be unlikely to make an observation of any phenomenon that is not already known. His Natural History is, in fact, doomed in practice to incompleteness, to repetition, to obscurity. It becomes a solemn trifling.

Contrast this rather gloomy picture with that of one who chooses to study any one of the groups included in this book. He finds that, for many of them, Great Britain contains fewer than fifty different forms; so that it is often possible to obtain, in the course of a year or two, a very high proportion of the entire British population by search in a single neighbourhood. To give an example of this: the number of British harvest-spiders known in 1928 was nineteen, and in that year the writer took nine of these within the confines of his half-acre garden.

Again, it will almost certainly be found that among British naturalists fewer than half-a-dozen are simultaneously engaged in active investigation of the group chosen. These ladies and gentlemen will be regarded by the beginner as authorities, and will be invested with all the glamour that authority commands; but he will find, if he is really serious in his work, that these same authorities will from the first welcome him as a colleague, that they will never regard him as a competitor or an interloper, and that they will always be ready with help, advice and encouragement. This, at least, has been the writer's own experience, for which he cannot be too grateful. A time will very soon come when these same authorities will address the newcomer as an equal, will share their good news with him; and he will find that he is well on the way to becoming an authority himself. That is not an end necessarily to be sought, but, should it be attained, it is a state from which it is reasonable to draw a modest satisfaction. It gives the student a proper sense of pride in his work, he feels that the torch of learning has been handed on and that it is now his responsibility to keep it trimmed and to help to bear it for a part of its way.

It should be evident that to the natural historian himself there is nothing but advantage to be gained by his adopting the course suggested in this book, but it would be wrong to think that the gain is all on one side. There is a proportionate gain to Science as a whole. Anyone working seriously at any of the groups mentioned in the following pages is certain to discover new facts and to extend the boundaries of existing knowledge, even if he does not make the discovery that is so often hailed as the highest possible achievement—which it is not—the discovery of a species new to Science. And indeed the contributions that "amateur" Natural History Societies have made to Biology in the past are well known to have been considerable.

It is particularly to be observed that all the groups in this book are groups of common animals. One of the most conspicuous fallacies among naturalists and others is that the commonplace is negligible and that the rarity is the only thing that matters. Henri Fabre has abundantly proved and has often reiterated the fact that what is common is not necessarily unimportant; and it would not be altogether wrong to say that what is commonest is necessarily the most important. Yet this fact has been so often and so widely overlooked that most of our familiar animals are those of which our ignorance is relatively greatest. Nor is this true only of our inconspicuous "small animals"; for it would not be easy to find a better example of this truth than the Adelie penguin. The Adelie penguin has been so successfully studied by a relatively small number of Antarctic explorers that we really know more about the life and habits of a penguin than about many of the birds that live in our own woods and fields.

Our thesis, then, is this—that there is abundant opportunity for personal enjoyment and a lasting satisfaction to be gained from the study of a group of small and common animals; that this enjoyment, satisfaction, and even pride, is proportional to the extent to which one concentrates on a single group; for such concentration results in one's becoming a specialist, or perhaps an authority, and will undoubtedly result in the advancement of biological science.

At this point it is well to outline the task that the naturalist sets himself. Its stages can be distinguished and described as follows— i. Choice of group. ii. Consultation of existing literature thereon. iii. Collection of local species. iv. Dissection and study of structure. v. Identification of species. vi. Study of habits and life-histories. These stages receive separate consideration in later chapters of this book; a few generalisations must be given here to complete this introductory chapter.

The naturalist's first necessity is to choose the order or family of animals in which he proposes to specialise. No advice can be given as to how this is to be done. The group may be one of those included in Part II of this book, or it may not; in any case the actual choice is so personal a matter that very little help can be offered. Sometimes the selection is the result of suggestion; sometimes it seems to be the result of a purely chance meeting with a specimen of the group. It is interesting to recall that Prof. J. C. Chamberlin of Oregon, the world's greatest authority on false-scorpions, has recorded the fact that his first sight of one of these little creatures in 1917 determined the direction of his life's work.

Secondly, a study of the existing literature of the group should be made, for only in this way can the naturalist learn how and where his animals can be found, how they are to be distinguished from other animals, how many species there are thought to be in Britain and in Europe and in the world, and how many unsolved problems their biology still holds. The naturalist need have no fear that of any British animal our knowledge is nearing completion: in fact the extent of our ignorance is often unbelievable. Many years ago the present writer was temporarily interested in woodlice, and sought from a leading authority on woodlice a list of the names of the British species. His reply was—"I could give you a list of the woodlice of almost any other country, but not of Britain." There are still animals of which this is true: for example it is much easier to turn up information about Antarctic sea-spiders (Pycnogonida) than to find out much about the British ones.

Simultaneously with this first approach to printed records, the naturalist will be anxious to go out and collect some specimens, or some more specimens, from his neighbourhood. The actual methods of collecting are described in Chapter 4; but some generalisations are needed here. It is an important feature common to all the groups chosen for this book that no objection can reasonably be raised if the collector wishes for any purpose to accumulate a large number of specimens.

It is otherwise with birds' eggs and butterflies. Bird populations have suffered untold damage at the hands of collectors and rare butterflies have been exterminated from their circumscribed areas before now in the same way, and these catastrophes, regretted too late, were inexcusable and indefensible. But no one can say that a collector who wants twenty earwigs or thirty ants or fifty woodlice should limit himself to half-a-dozen. In all these lesser known groups of small invertebrates, a long series has a real value in making plain the variations due to age, sex or locality, as well as in providing sufficient material for morphological studies.

When the collected specimens have been brought home they will need examination and identification. For this purpose magnification is necessary, and a simple hand-lens is the first essential of the naturalist. It reveals much, and with practice it comes, surprisingly, to reveal more and more; indeed in the last century many naturalists did an astonishing amount of work with single lenses which they preferred to the microscopes of their time. Few to-day would be found to share this opinion, and the use of the microscope is more fully described in Chapter 6. There is one aspect of microscopy, however, which may be mentioned here—it is the incredible beauty which the miscroscope makes visible.

Through its lenses we see not only the functional beauty that emerges from the perfect adaptation of a limb or an organ to its task, but also an unsuspected beauty of design on the smallest scale, usually with no manifest purpose and no likelihood of being perceived or appreciated save by the enquiring mind of the occasional naturalist. One ought to feel that one is being privileged to see creations of Nature that are normally hidden from the majority of mankind.

But even a biologist does not use a microscope for aesthetic pleasure: he examines animals partly because he wishes to know the details of the way they are made, and partly because he must know their names. Unless the name of a species is known, most of the knowledge we have gained about it is useless: we cannot discover whether it was known already, and if so how much was known already; and we cannot easily describe our observations and opinions to others.

Many of the animals described in this book are fairly easy to name, and the general method to be followed is given in Chapter 7. It is usually best and sometimes necessary to use a killed specimen; living things are inclined to resent the liberties that one is forced to take with their intimate structure and do not willingly co-operate at their christenings. One requires, too, a certain amount of experience in the handling of small animals, experience which rapidly comes with practice.

It is very necessary to resist the temptation to think that when a specimen has been named the end has been reached. Actually it is the beginning, for it is now that one can usefully begin to investigate its behaviour, its habits, its mode of life, in fact the whole of its "natural history" as a living thing. This can often be done satisfactorily while the animals are in captivity, and the task of providing them with suitable cages in which they will be comfortable and will act normally is one of the most fascinating sides of experimental biology. It is also one of the most fruitful in leading to the discovery of facts previously unknown.

This survey of the whole field of study which interest in a single group of animals will provide shows that, quite obviously, it is not an occupation for a few weeks in the summer. There is something to be done all the year round, for this sort of natural history also encourages craftsmanship. There are cages to be made, apparatus of many kinds to be constructed, in fact the whole technique of laboratory arts to be mastered. An active naturalist is constantly hatching ideas, and almost always the execution of such ideas requires a piece of apparatus which cannot be bought. It must be made, tried, improved and made again; and always the essentials of one's experience should be recorded in writing. A naturalist's note-books are vitally important; they alone can guard against lapses of memory which occur with a lamentable frequency; they are, in fact, his brains. Finally, it may perhaps be added that an interest in work of this kind may well survive the passage of years, and grow into a source of contentment for life.

It has, indeed, the possibility of more than this. I have briefly referred above to the unsuspected beauty which the microscope reveals when small animals are examined with its help. In returning to this matter I want to quote a few lines from the first page of Miss Monica Dickens' novel, *The Happy Prisoner*.

[The moth] "was lying with wings half spread, the corners of the lower ones just showing inside the upper. They appeared to be made up of thousands of tiny fibres, weaving a pattern in browns and fawns that was like a priceless shawl or piece of tapestry. At the edges, which were shaped like shells, with a tuft of down between each scallop, the fibres blended into a frieze of darker brown, which was continued at exactly the same point on the lower wings, so that when the two were spread the pattern would be continuous.... If this pattern had been on a shawl or tapestry, it would have taken months or years of patient eye-straining toil. It might have been someone's life-work, someone who would go blind over it and die without ever knowing that it was destined to endure and to be treasured for hundreds of years. But Nature could afford to squander it on an ephemeral thing like a moth, which, far from being treasured, was discouraged with camphor and closed windows."

Here we read the feelings of a sensitive mind, expressed in the chosen words of a writer of literature; words which show us the kind of admiration which the bodies of these unimportant creatures may evoke. A Lord Grey may write *In Praise of Birds* and find an expectant audience more than half ready to agree with him; but there is, in fact, a greater opportunity for one who can convince his friends or his readers that there is as much to be said "In Praise of Woodlice." Herein lies by far the greatest of the possibilities of small animals.

Chapter II

SMALL ANIMALS: THEIR CHARACTERISTICS

A STUDY of the early stages in the evolution of animals gives an impression of perpetual experiment in the production of new forms of animal life, as if some Omnipotent Power were driving living matter to continuous change, persuading it to assume all possible shapes and coaxing it to occupy all available situations. This is, of course, an allegory. We do not know the nature of the suggested Power, nor whether it works on living things from without or springs up within themselves, or both; but we can use the idea to help us to understand the variety of living things that the world contains.

Living matter seems to have yielded to this Power; and, in spite of the ease with which animals may be killed, in spite of the difficulties produced by heat and cold, by flood and drought, and in spite of constant opposition and competition from each other, to have created a large number of different sorts of animals, which have colonised every corner of the globe and adopted every imaginable way of living.

Two features of this cosmic process become clear when it is examined in greater detail.

The first is that these experiments, if they may so be termed, have been followed by very different degrees of success. Animals of many kinds have appeared for relatively short spaces of time and, for some reason at which we may or may not be able to guess, have disappeared. Only the buried relics which we call fossils remain, to tell us all we know about creatures that are now extinct. Others have done rather more : they have advanced a certain way and then they have stopped. They have, as it were, struck a balance between the urge to change and to spread and the difficulties of changing and spreading, and so they have lived on in a state of equilibrium. They have survived, but survived pointlessly—so far as we can tell.

The last sentence introduces the second feature of evolution. We can detect no evidence of purpose behind it all. Any purpose mentioned in the story of the evolution of animals is either a metaphor, just a convenient form of words, or it is a purpose that has been read into the story by man himself. It is rather difficult to accept the idea of a purposeless activity, and purpose perhaps there is; but perhaps the Omnipotent Purpose behind the operations of the Universe, of which animal evolution is a part, is a purpose beyond our understanding. Mankind has long striven to describe the Universe in the simple terms of some comprehensible plan, but there is no evidence that such a description could be simple, or even that it could be comprehensible. We just do not know.

Among the early experiments in the making of animals, there appeared one feature that was an undoubted and conspicuous success. This was the idea of the body-segment, the self-contained unit of structure, with gut and nerves, blood-vessels, excretory and reproductive organs almost complete. An animal could be made by joining together a number of these segments, or more accurately by allowing them to grow, one after the other, from some suitable origin; and the most familiar example of an animal built to such a specification is the common earthworm.

The success of this design was due largely to the fact that it could be at once followed by a distinction between head and tail. In the alternative, animals were developing on a radially-symmetrical plan, such as persists to-day in the starfish, the sea-anemone and the coral. Animals of this kind were either stationary, fixed to one spot throughout most of their lives, or they drifted vaguely in the water, at the mercy of the waves and currents, with very little control over their movements. These animals were incapable of further development; they are an example of futile survival.

The segmented worm, however, had great possibilities. Anyone can see that the earthworm of his garden suffers from having a soft and almost unprotected body, and is handicapped by the lack of reasonable limbs. Therefore in the next advance two additions appeared.

Protection was obtained by a hardening of the cuticle, impregnating it with chalk, or with a complex nitrogenous compound called chitin. The chalk, which was derived from the sea, is found familiarly in the strong armour of the lobster and in a less rigid form in the coating of many marine animals. Chitin is not such a hard substance; it is tough or leathery and very resistant to chemical reagents.

If a number of cockroaches or spiders are thoroughly boiled in caustic soda solution, all the muscles and other soft organs within are dissolved and empty skeletons remain. If they are then bleached with hydrogen peroxide and warmed with a strong acid they too will dissolve, and if now the acid is neutralised the chitin is precipitated as a white powder. When it is formed naturally in the cuticle of a small animal it provides a very efficient protection. It also prevents or retards the loss of water from the living tissues, an ever-present problem for land-dwelling creatures.

Secondly the simple primitive limbs were developed into jointed ones, similarly armoured, and they were gradually modified into various forms, some being designed for walking, some for swimming, some as weapons and, most important of all, some as "jaws" or mouth-parts for seizing living prey, biting solid food or imbibing liquids.

At the same time, the segments themselves were modified. Some, particularly those at the hinder end, shed their limbs; some grew broader, some contracted, and some were closely bunched together to form a distinctive fraction of the body, such as the head or thorax. In particular it was of obvious value to have at one end a definite head, which carried eyes and other sense-organs and was normally in front when the animal moved.

It should be clear that this general account of bodily structure includes the bodies of all the familiar insects as well as their closest relatives the centipedes and millipedes, the spiders and scorpions, the crabs and lobsters. All these are contained in the great group of animals called the Arthropoda, meaning "jointed legs."

These arthropods are completely world-wide. That they have covered the whole of what is usually referred to as "the habitable globe" goes without saying; in addition they are found in all the seas and oceans, from the tropics to the poles. They have made their way to oceanic islands, long separated by great distances from the continents; they have colonised dark caves and explored the burning deserts. In the frozen Arctic they abound as far north as the land stretches; in the colder Antarctic they are the only permanent inhabitants of the continent. No other group of animals can boast a distribution like this.

Their supremacy is even more marked when the number of species is considered. Men have been collecting and describing animals ever since Aristotle laid the foundations of zoology 350 years before Christ, and in twenty-three centuries they have named well over a million different kinds. More than half of these are arthropods; and there is no doubt that many more remain to be described—they are, in fact, being discovered in considerable numbers every day.

Success of this sort forces itself more and more upon the attention of man. Everywhere and always man must take account of small animals, which continuously attack his person, infect his herds, ruin his crops and deplete his stores. The damage they do amounts to a loss of many millions of pounds a year and renders futile a very appreciable fraction of man's efforts. How is it that man is able to retain his supremacy? Why is it that the arthropod is not master of the earth?

There are two reasons for this, reasons which have set a limit to the insurgence of arthropod life. The first is a mental or psychological one. It is customary to hear of the "marvels of instinct," but not quite so usual to hear of the limitations of instinctive behaviour. The behaviour of small animals is almost wholly instinctive, which means that they are richly endowed with inherited capacities to carry out the necessary and sometimes complicated activities involved in nest-making, egg-laying and so on. They seem to do these things as if driven by an irresistible urge, which arises at the appropriate time, or is called up by the appropriate stimulus; and in general they pursue any operation to its end with no change in method, even in changed circumstances. This serves them well enough in all ordinary conditions, but whenever a problem has to be solved, or whenever wisdom gained from past experience might be used in the face of a difficulty, the arthropod is usually found to be at a disadvantage. This is a contrast to the habits and actions of birds and mammals. These have bigger brains; they inherit a relatively small endowment of instinctive behaviour, but they possess the power to learn, to learn intelligently and to profit from what they have learnt. For this reason they stand a far better chance of survival in a world of changing scenes and problems.

The second reason is a mechanical one. Arthropods are nearly all small animals and their size is limited. This is a consequence of their construction, described earlier in this chapter, a peculiarity of which is that support and protection are provided by an outside skeleton of dead matter. This rigid skeleton prevents the con-

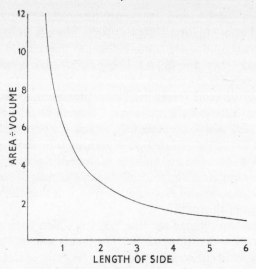

FIG. I.—The Relation between Length, Area and Volume

tinuous growth to which we are accustomed, and a different method appears. As the animal grows its skeleton gets tighter and tighter: finally a time comes when the skeleton splits and there emerges through the split, more or less slowly, a larger animal with a new skeleton, which is at first quite soft. This operation of moulting, or ecdysis, is a serious one, and the animal usually hides itself in a suitable shelter for the occasion and remains in shelter there until the new skeleton has had time to harden.

Now as the size of an animal increases, its weight increases at a greater rate than its area, so that larger animals need disproportionately thicker skeletons than smaller ones, and these skeletons take disproportionately longer to harden. An insect as big as a large dog, for example, might well have to spend a quarter or a third of its life waiting for successive skeletons to harden. Not only would this be a serious disadvantage, but in addition the heavy body would collapse or slump while it was still soft and a permanent shape could not be maintained.

Small animals often make up in numbers what they lack in size, and so attain astonishing results, but the fact remains that 15 cm. is about the maximum length—and one very rarely reached—for a land-dwelling arthropod. Those that live in water can grow larger, because of the support which the water gives them.

This relationship between area and volume (or between surface and weight) is so important, and occurs so often in biology, and in other sciences too, that it deserves more consideration. A cube has six faces, and if the length of a side is 1 cm. it has a total surface area of 6 sq. cm. for a volume of 1 c.c. If its side is 2 cm. long its area is 24 sq. cm. and its volume is 8 c.c., that is to say not 6 but only 3 sq. cm. of surface for each c.c. of volume. It is very interesting to make out a table showing the relation between surface and volume for cubes of different sizes, and to express their relation as a graph (Fig. 1).

Length of side	Total area	Volume	$\dfrac{\text{Area}}{\text{Volume}}$
·01	·0006	·000001	600
·1	·06	·001	60
·25	·375	·015625	24
·5	1·5	·125	12
1·0	6·0	1·0	6
2·0	24·0	8·0	3
3·0	54·0	27·0	2
4·0	96·0	64·0	1·5
5·0	150·0	125·0	1·2
6·0	216·0	216·0	1·0
10·0	600·0	1000·0	·6

Other consequences of an increase in size are to be found in the internal organisation of the body. When the body is very small and the surface is relatively large, oxygen can diffuse into the body and carbon dioxide can escape from it at a rate which is great enough to permit all the respiration needed to liberate the energy necessary for the animal's life. But with larger bodies the surface-exchange will not suffice for this, and hence there is found some form of transport system for taking oxygen to the tissues, for removing carbon dioxide and nitrogenous waste from them, for distributing food from the digestive tract to the distant organs and for ridding the whole complex organisation of its waste.

In this book we shall not in general be concerned with the internal organs, but it is well to remember their existence and to understand why they are necessary in all animals except the very smallest.

Chapter III

SMALL ANIMALS: THEIR RELATIONSHIPS

THERE are, as has been said, more than a million different sorts of animals, a number so large that it is not possible for a naturalist to study or even to get to know them all. This is a difficulty which is familiar in all branches of science, and it can be met only by putting animals into groups and studying the group as a unit, choosing a few animals from it as representatives. This is legitimate because examination of the bodies of animals makes it clear that they show various degrees of resemblance and difference, which have been used by zoologists to arrange them in a system of classification in which their relationships are expressed.

When this is done it becomes evident that in the animal kingdom there are about a dozen great groups, the animals in which show recognisable similarities, but the relationships between the different groups is so obscure as to be little more than a matter of speculation.

These more or less independent groups are called phyla, singular phylum, derived from the Greek phylon, a branch; and the animals with which this book deals include representatives of three different phyla, called the Annelida, the Arthropoda and the Mollusca.

This idea of grouping together animals which show certain degrees of resemblance can be repeated with successively greater attention to details, so that each phylum can be itself divided and subdivided in several stages. To each stage of subdivision a name is given, and in all phyla the names are taken in the same order. Thus phyla are divided into classes, classes into orders, orders into families, families into genera and genera into species.

This system of six categories was worked out at the end of the eighteenth and beginning of the nineteenth centuries, chiefly by the famous Swedish biologist Carl Linnaeus. Closer study of animals since then has made it necessary to increase the number above six, at least in some of the phyla. This is done by the addition of the prefix super- or sub- to any of the existing names, so that in an extreme case the complete range might be—phylum, sub-phylum, super-class, class, sub-class, super-order, order, sub-order, super-family, family, sub-family, super-genus, genus, sub-genus, species, sub-species. The term super-genus is not, or is extremely rarely, used, but all the fifteen others are quite usual, and give sufficient grading for most zoologists. Even so, it is not impossible to find such additions as grade, cohort and super-cohort, for some systematists seem to aim at greater and greater precision.

This fact should make it easy to realise that even the original steps, class, order, family and genus, have not equivalent values in different phyla, or, to put it another way, there is no recognised or definable degree of difference which either demands or justifies the creation of a new order or a new class. One zoologist may examine the characteristics of twenty genera and decide that they make a convenient and homogeneous family; a second, looking at the same animals, may prefer to put them into three or four families and perhaps even to distinguish one of them by making a separate sub-order for it. It is a matter of personal opinion, and depends on the emphasis which either worker lays on the characteristics themselves. A student, perplexed, might enquire of them both, "How important is the difference between long smooth legs and short hairy ones?" and receive quite different answers. Later generations may choose to accept the opinion of one rather than the other, either because of convenience or because one author had a wider reputation for wisdom, or because he expressed his ideas more persuasively or in more widely read journals.

The truth is that Nature made the animals and man made zoology: more particularly man made systematics. To classify things is a well-marked tendency of the human mind; Nature never classifies. In fact she produces countless intermediates and exceptions, which are constantly upsetting our careful schemes; she rides roughshod over the parallel lines between our contrasting columns and shows no sympathy for our orderly and ordered arrangements.

This depressing picture is perhaps not quite so true of the unit which the biologist calls a species. A species is, in ordinary speech, a distinct sort or kind of animal or plant. The idea of a species was first properly expressed by Linnaeus in the eighteenth century, and it was usually taken as a sufficient definition of a species that all individuals of a species could breed together, and produce fertile offspring. Thus all horses, whether heavy-draught Clydesdales or light polo ponies, are one species, Equus caballus, just as all dogs, from Irish wolf-hounds to Skye-terriers, are one species, Canis familiaris. Clearly, within a species a considerable range of variation can exist, and biologists have been at some pains to formulate a satisfactory definition of the word. Two definitions which are widely known are:

"The perennial succession of similar individuals perpetuated by generation" (de Jussieu), and

"A community whose distinctive morphological characteristics are, in the opinion of a competent systematist, sufficiently definite to entitle it to a specific name." (Tate Regan.)

As an illustration of how all this works out in practice, the zoological position of the common Garden Spider may be given.

Phylum	Arthropoda	Sub-order	Araneomorphae
Sub-phylum	Chelicerata	Super-family	Argiopiformia
Class	Arachnida	Family	Argiopidae
Sub-class	Caulogastra	Sub-family	Araneinae
Super-order	Sternifera	Genus	Araneus
Order	Araneae	Species	diadematus

Thus the specific name of this well-known and beautiful spider is Araneus diadematus. The first word Araneus is the generic name, used by a Swedish zoologist, C. Clerck, in 1757; the second, diadematus, is called the trivial name or specific epithet; in this case it also was used by Clerck.

This convenient method of giving every animal and plant a name composed of two Latin words is the essence of the system of binomial nomenclature, first properly worked out by Linnaeus. Very often the name of the zoologist who originally described and named the species is added—thus, Araneus diadematus Clerck. This is important when two or more writers have used the same name for two specimens which were subsequently found to be of different species.

The specific epithet should always be written or printed with a small letter, even when it is derived from a proper name, and there should be no comma between it and the name of the author.

Sometimes a genus grows to such a size that, purely for convenience, it is "revised" and several genera are created out of it.

One of these must continue to bear the original name; but the names of all species in the new genera will be changed. They will of course retain their specific epithets, though possibly changed in gender, and the author's name is then printed in parentheses. For example, the species first described by Simon as Liobunum silvaticum was, in full, Liobunum silvaticum Sim., but when transferred to a new genus Nelima it became Nelima silvatica (Sim.).

Whenever for any reason an animal's name is changed, its other names become synonyms, and so many adventures befall the names of animals that most species carry with them a list of synonyms, evidence of past baptisms.

It used at one time to be the custom for writers to apologise for the use of binomial Latin names for animals that have no common English names, just as it used to be the habit of the plain man to laugh at the idea that a microscopic creature should have such a high-sounding title, but with the spread of biological education these days have passed, and all recognise the advantages of the Linnaean system.

The animals described in the second part of this book belong to the phyla Annelida, Arthropoda and Mollusca.

ANNELIDA

The name of the phylum Annelida means the ring-like animals and is derived from the Latin annulus, a ring and the Greek * eidos, resemblance. The rings in question are, of course, the segments of the body which were described in Chapter 2, where the earthworm was mentioned as a familiar example of an animal in which the segments are particularly obvious; and in fact the phylum Annelida includes the earthworm and its allies.

It should be noted that the simple word "worm" is hardly ever used in zoology, where it has no definite meaning. Originally it was applied to any animal whose length was much greater than its breadth—thus Milton makes Adam say:

"O Eve, in evil hour didst thou give ear
To that foul worm"

---

* It is therefore a hybrid word, that is, a word derived from two different languages. In biology and in other sciences it is often necessary to invent new words, and many authorities object to words of hybrid origin. They should be avoided whenever possible, but it is not always easy to do so.

where "worm" means snake or serpent. Linnaeus put all the long
thin invertebrates into a class called Vermes, literally translated
worms, but we now find that the worm-like animals are really so
different that they have been put into several different phyla, and
the "Vermes" have disappeared.

All the Annelida have bodies that are covered and to some slight
extent protected by a thin cuticle which is largely composed of
chitin. (See page 19.) Beneath this is a skin or epidermis, usually
containing simple glands which secrete a fluid over the animal's
body and which cover a set of circular muscles running round the
body and a set of longitudinal muscles running up and down it.
Piercing epidermis and cuticle there are spike- or blade-like
organs, which act as primitive limbs or legs and are called either
by the Latin name setae or the Greek name chaetae. We always
tend to think of earthworms as having no limbs, but this is not
quite true and in fact they have more limbs than snakes or slow-
worms.

The phylum Annelida is divided into four classes, only three of
which need be mentioned here. They are called the Polychaeta
("many bristles"), the Oligochaeta ("few bristles") and the Hirudinea (the leeches).

The Polychaeta live in the sea. The "head" in the front of the
body is usually obvious and different from the segments behind
it; it sometimes carries tentacles and eyes, and the egg hatches into
a larva which swims freely in the water. This class contains the
"rag-worm" or "lug-worm" which fishermen often use as bait.

The Oligochaeta live either underground or in fresh water. The
head is not so conspicuous as in the marine worms. The eggs are
laid in cocoons and hatch into small worms. We shall be more
fully concerned with Oligochaeta in Part II.

The Hirudinea or Leeches have no setae. They have two
suckers, one at each end of the body, for they are parasites, living
on the blood of their hosts, with which they gorge themselves.

ARTHROPODA

The phylum Arthropoda owes its name to its jointed limbs—
arthron, a joint; pous, podos, a foot. Like the Annelida of the
previous phylum, the bodies of all Arthropoda are more or less
clearly segmented, but certain very obvious advances distinguish
the two groups.

In the first place the body is better protected, so that the Arthropoda are sometimes described as "animals in armour."

Secondly, the segments of the arthropod body are often very different from each other, and they are arranged in groups which thus divide the body into regions in a way unknown among the annelids. Any familiar insect will be recognised by the reader as possessing a head, a thorax and an abdomen; in fact its very name insect, derived from seco, I cut, refers to this dividing. It is not obvious that the head has been made from seven segments, as it is; it is more obvious that the thorax consists of three, each of which carries a pair of legs; and the abdomen is based on eleven segments, some of which are often missing.

Thirdly, this tendency to modification spreads to the limbs. In an ideally primitive arthropod there should be a pair of jointed limbs to each segment, and the limbs would probably be nearly all legs, used for walking or swimming. But on the head of the animal these limbs are usually profoundly changed and have become "jaws" and accessories to the jaws, preferably described as "mouth-parts." As such they show a very great diversity among the many different kinds of arthropods, and are to be found variously adapted for biting, piercing or sucking. Thus their study is often a matter of great importance. It is also extremely interesting to see how the same basic plan can be adapted to serve such different purposes. By shortening a segment here, broadening a segment there, by omitting this portion or by dividing that, results are obtained which differ in appearance as much as do the biting mouth-parts of an earwig and the piercing stylets of a gnat and which yet have a clear relationship with each other.

These features, and others, are no doubt responsible for the great success of the phylum Arthropoda, which contains more than half the known species of animals in the world. These are grouped into six classes, five of which are well known to everyone—

> Crustacea
> Insecta
> Arachnida
> Chilopoda
> Diplopoda.

The class Crustacea includes the crabs and lobsters, crayfish, shrimps and prawns and a multitude of smaller and less generally familiar creatures in salt and fresh water. The crustaceans have typically two pairs of antennae, and the three pairs of head-appendages which form the mouth-parts are often assisted by some of the appendages of the front segments of the thorax. In the more highly evolved forms, represented by the stalk-eyed lobsters, crabs, etc., the head of six segments and the thorax of eight are fused together to make a cephalothorax and covered over by a single carapace. The abdomen consists of six segments.

Among the unusual crustaceans are the barnacles, which when adult lead a sedentary life, and the woodlice, which are almost the only crustaceans that live on land.

The class Insecta requires no introduction, and the main structural feature of the body of an insect—its division into seven, three and eleven segments—was mentioned above. In addition it should be mentioned that in insects there is one pair of antennae and that the thorax typically bears two pairs of wings. We shall meet, however, in this book insects which have no wings as well as insects which have only two.

A more important difference among the various orders of insects is found in their life-histories. Nearly all insects lay eggs and from the eggs of the more primitive insects there hatches a little creature which resembles its parents more or less closely, save in size and sexual immaturity. As it grows it is therefore concerned solely with increase in bulk, not with change of form. The young of such insects are known as nymphs. The eggs of the more advanced kinds of insects hatch as larvae, that is to say as creatures which bear no apparent resemblance to their adults; and very often they pass into a resting or pupal stage before the mature form appears. The caterpillar and chrysalis of a butterfly are, of course, the most familiar example of this type of life-history; and it should be remembered that many animals begin their lives as larvae, which are often more active forms than the adults, vigorously concerned with dispersal and feeding.

Insects are everywhere. If it were possible for a man to see, in one world-wide glance, all the animals on the earth, and if he were able at the same time to rid himself of all prejudice in favour of the class, the mammals, to which he belongs, he would assuredly get an impression of a world inhabited by insects.

The class Arachnida, like the insects and unlike the crustaceans, is almost unknown in the sea. It includes the spiders, harvestmen, scorpions, mites and ticks, as well as other rather unfamiliar forms, all of which are contained in twelve orders comprising at least forty thousand species. In the body of an arachnid there is only one constriction, a "waist" or pedicle, separating a cephalothorax from an abdomen, but the pedicle is absent from many forms. There are no antennae. The mouth is provided with a pair of chelicerae, behind which is a pair of organs known as pedipalpi. These are sometimes leg-like tactile organs, sometimes pincer-like, as in the scorpions. There are four pairs of legs. The abdomen has usually no limbs or appendages, but the silk spinnerets of spiders provide an exception to this. Nearly all Arachnida lay eggs, which hatch as nymphs, not as larvae.

Until recently zoologists used to recognise among the Arthropoda a class called the Myriapoda, in which there were two subclasses, the Chilopoda containing the centipedes and the Diplopoda, or millipedes. There are, however, such far-reaching differences between the two groups that it is now more usual to make them into two distinct classes. Both are well known and widely distributed and are to be found in all conditions in both fertile and barren districts.

In both classes there is one pair of antennae; the head is clearly distinguished from the following segments, all of which bear limbs. In the centipedes the appendages of the first segment are modified to form poison-fangs, for the animals are carnivorous. There is one pair of legs on each of the remaining segments. In the millipedes, which are vegetarians, there are no poison-fangs and most of the segments bear two pairs of legs each.

MOLLUSCA

The third phylum with which we are concerned is the Mollusca or shell-fish, animals which in many ways are different from the Arthropoda, but which also show the necessity for protecting their soft bodies. These bodies show no trace of segmentation; they are usually covered in a fold of skin, called the mantle, which secretes the shell, the feature by which most molluscs are ordinarily recognised.

The body of a mollusc is usually divisible into three parts, called the foot, the head and the visceral hump, the relative importance of which is different in the different classes. In the class Cephalopoda, which includes the octopuses and squids, the head is large and the foot is divided and drawn out into the tentacles with which the prey is captured. In the class Lamellibranchiata, or bivalves, the head is reduced and the foot is hatchet- or wedge-shaped. In the class Gastropoda, or snails, both head and foot are conspicuous and the visceral hump is twisted into a spiral.

All the animals included in Part II belong to one of these three phyla, and a systematic guide to them would read as follows:

		PHYLUM	CLASS	ORDER	BRITISH SPECIES
1	Earthworms	Annelida	Oligochaeta		25
2	Woodlice	Arthropoda	Crustacea	Isopoda	37
3	Silver Fish	,,	Insecta	Thysanura	23
4	Earwigs	,,	,,	Dermaptera	8
5	Cockroaches	,,	,,	Orthoptera	8
6	Ants	,,	,,	Hymenoptera	36
7	Dragonflies	,,	,,	Odonata	43
8	Mosquitoes	,,	,,	Diptera	28
9	Centipedes	,,	Chilopoda		38
10	Harvestmen	,,	Arachnida	Opiliones	21
11	False-scorpions	,,	,,	Chelonethi	24
12	Slugs	Mollusca	Pulmonata		24

The numbers in the last column must not be taken as undoubtedly accurate. I can assure my readers that the numbers quoted for Harvestmen and False-scorpions are correct for 1953, but both these numbers have changed more than once during my own lifetime. They change because a new species is discovered, or because a name is found to be covering two species, or because two species believed to be different are found to be the same. The numbers quoted for the other groups are not necessarily as recent as this, though every effort has been made to be as reasonably up to date as possible. Nevertheless, the specialists in these other groups may well wish to change them, and it does not follow that they will all wish to make the same changes. There is never a "last word" in Biology.

Common Earthworm (*Lumbricus*).

Earthworms. A group of specimens, some mature (with saddle).

Earthworms mating. The animals are hermaphroditic and each fertilises the other.

Chapter IV

SMALL ANIMALS: THEIR COLLECTION

THE first thing that every practical biologist must do is to obtain his living material, animal or plant, in a state suitable for examination. Unless he is a student, or is otherwise unusually favoured by circumstance, this means that he must collect it himself—with trawl or dredge he must search the seas, with net he must scour the lakes and rivers, with sieve or sweep he must comb the undergrowth, the hedges and ditches, the humus. These are the activities of the more fortunate hunters; others must scrutinise small vessels of liquid through their microscopes or explore the insides of the bodies of larger animals, not always freshly killed, for invading parasites.

The straightforward open-air collector is much to be envied. His pursuits may take him to the more attractive parts of the country, to the shores or the hills, to the moors or the forests or the rivers. And even the more modest searcher, who does no more than bicycle to the nearest stretch of country, is luckier than the chemist in his malodorous laboratory or the financier in his city office.

Moreover, there is an inherent joy about collecting material objects, whatever they may be. It is not, perhaps, a sensation that is easily explained, for it is quite distinct from the mere desire to acquire possessions and then to accumulate more and more. The joy lies partly in the chase itself, partly in the satisfaction of coming upon the "living treasure" in spite of its ability to hide and to escape. Furthermore, and distinct again, there is a very curious satisfaction that follows the finding of certain particular species. Some species seem to acquire a special glamour giving them an added desirability, so that one is perpetually pleased when one meets them. Even if one refrains from collecting them unnecessarily, one feels glad to have seen them again. The cause of this individual attractiveness is very hard to understand, but that it exists, surrounding certain animals and yet missing from their relatives, is a fact to which all collectors of animals will bear witness.

It may be mentioned that these irresistible species are not necessarily the rarities which are universally valued for that reason. Rarity is not a biological feature, and is a quality that is often ascribed to a species by writers without a full understanding of what the term implies. An object may be rare in the sense that First Folios of Shakespeare are rare, because there are but a few examples still in existence: an animal may be rare because it is on the verge of extinction and, like the early Shakespeares, only a few specimens are surviving; or an animal may be described as "rare" because one specimen was captured in 1834, a second in 1879, a third in 1901 and a fourth in 1948.

This last sort of rarity is ascribed to animals of many kinds. It may be due to the fact that the animal has a restricted range and a localised distribution, like the spider Dolomedes fimbriatus; or because it is nocturnal in habits and is therefore seldom seen, like the spider Oonops domesticus; or because the animal has such efficient concealing colours or protective devices that it is difficult to catch, like the spider Hyptiotes paradoxus; or it may simply mean that only a few people have been interested in the animal, and so only a very few have ever tried to catch it. Whatever be the explanation of the rarity in any one case, it is most probable that it is apparent rather than real. If a species has really persisted in Britain for a century or more, even though it has been observed but seldom during that time, it is obvious that many individuals must have existed so that the sexes may have met and sufficient offspring have been produced to ensure survival. Thus it often happens that when an enthusiast comes into the neighbourhood of a reputably rare species, he finds that by looking in the right place at the right time it may be found in considerable numbers and that actually it is not rare at all.

The equipment with which the collector sets out on his visit to hedge and ditch is usually simple—the simpler the better. He will need something in which to bring home the specimens he wishes to keep alive, and for this purpose may choose between glass-topped pill-boxes or corked specimen-tubes. On the whole the latter are better. They are less fragile and a dozen or more packed into a flat cigarette tin travel far more easily in the coat-pocket. For animals which are killed at once, a cyanide bottle for insects or a bottle of spirit for those with softer bodies is all that is necessary.

Something, however, will be required, in order to discover the animals. Most small invertebrates are found by the methods of beating, sweeping and sifting. In beating, hedges, shrubs and the lower branches of trees are beaten or shaken, while the collector holds beneath an inverted umbrella, or the lid of a cardboard box, or simply a folded newspaper. Sweeping is carried out with a stout canvas bag or "net" which is dragged through the undergrowth and long grass and periodically emptied on to the newspaper. Sweeping is always liable to injure some of the specimens: moreover, it does not reach the grass-roots, among which so many animals hide, and it is often worth while to adopt the slower method of patient search at ground level, turning over the leaves and coaxing the animals into a test-tube.

Small invertebrates are always to be obtained in large numbers and in surprising variety by the process of sifting. A sieve, as sold in a hardware shop for any ordinary purpose, is not a very convenient object to carry about, nor is it particularly suitable for biological work. The best thing to do is to take a piece of fine-meshed wire netting about eighteen inches square, fold it in half and fasten the folded ends together. This will open out into a boat-shaped sieve and lie flat again after use. Handfuls of fallen leaves, pine-needles and all kinds of vegetable débris are scooped into it and shaken over the newspaper or sheet.

Quantities of small animals descend. Always there are woodlice and centipedes; often there are leaping spring-tails and small two-winged flies which seem surprisingly to have been living in circumstances where their wings were of little use. There will be spiders and worms and slugs and sometimes small shells, and there will be beetles and false-scorpions and a host of things which one cannot recognise at sight.

It is very interesting to notice the different behaviour of all these creatures in response to the rude awakening they have experienced. Some of them, apparently unshaken, take themselves off at once: the spring-tails leap energetically, the flies fly, the centipedes and the woodlice and the spiders run away quickly, hastening to the edge of the sheet and diving for safety into the leaves beneath it. The worms wriggle protestingly and the mites run fussily about as if they do not know what to do. If they come upon a piece of wood or a dried leaf they run over and around it, unwilling to leave it and yet not sheltering below it. The harvest-

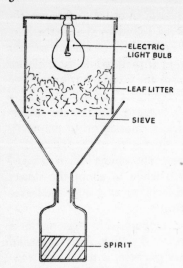

FIG. 2.—A Berlese Funnel

men and false-scorpions remain quiet, as if "winded" like a fallen cart-horse, but after a moment or two they recover and walk away.

In addition to these well-tried and straightforward methods of searching for small animals almost individually, there is a device which is becoming more and more widely known, used and appreciated. This is the apparatus known as a Berlese funnel (Fig. 2).

A Berlese funnel consists essentially of a vertical cylinder inside which is a horizontal sieve: above this there is an electric light bulb and below it a funnel-shaped exit leading to a bottle of alcohol. The dead leaves, moss, etc., among which the animals are living is put into the funnel and rests on the sieve; the light is then switched on. Nearly all the so-called cryptozoic fauna tend to move away from the light of the lamp and from the dryness which its warmth produces in the topmost layers. Thus they burrow lower and lower until they pass through the sieve and drop into the bottle of preservative.

The advantages in the use of a Berlese funnel are obvious. The work in the woods and fields is quicker and easier, for the filling of a sack or sandbag with leaves is less troublesome than the sifting of the same amount of material on the spot. It involves far less stooping to the ground and straightening of the back afterwards; which fact may make no appeal to the young, but as the years go by it becomes well worthy of consideration. When the ground seems to have become so much farther off than it was, and when the straightening of one's back is no longer accomplished without a twinge, or may to the "lumbagoid" suddenly be found to be impossible, then the value of the Berlese method is greatly enhanced.

Moreover, the material is more thoroughly searched by this means, and perhaps the greatest advantage of all is the fact that the sackload may be taken or sent home and need not necessarily be dealt with at once. It may wait in a corner of the laboratory and in a week or ten days it will probably be just as productive.

The construction of a Berlese funnel is simple. The size of the cylinder depends in part on the scale on which one is working, and in part on the particular animals being studied. It may in some cases be no larger than a domestic grocery "tin," 10 cm. or so in diameter, and some collectors use such a form in the field during their outdoor search for specimens. For the laboratory, a larger size is desirable—a five-gallon oil drum is suitable. Alternatively, an oil can may be adapted and has the advantage that its top is already funnel-shaped. It is turned upside down, its bottom is cut off and the sieve dropped in.

This is made either of wire gauze with quarter-inch mesh or of perforated zinc, cut to shape so as to rest securely at the top of the funnel. For the lamp a 40-watt bulb is strong enough, and many biologists recommend a 25-watt bulb and a longer exposure —up to 24 hours or even more. It is best to have the material not more than five or six inches deep and to arrange it in a centrally hollowed pile. This gives the animals freer access to the sieve and prevents their being trapped on the way in condensed moisture.

It is fairly obvious that the method most favoured by a collector must be one that is adapted to the general habits of the animal he is seeking, for one does not expect to find earthworms in the butterfly net nor dragonflies in a sieve; but it is also true that to break away from "tradition" and to try occasionally a little collecting by the wrong method in the wrong place is sometimes rewarded.

There is, finally, a feature about the collecting of animals of any group which cannot be omitted. Most of us tend to visit the same area, or the same small number of areas, and to collect there year after year: we go to places that are conveniently accessible, that are free from human interference, and have yielded us good harvests on our earliest visits. They may not be famous collecting grounds in the way that the New Forest and Burnham Beeches are famous, but they have a hold on our hearts and we remain faithful to them. It might well be thought that repeated collecting over the same tract of land would soon result in our having found every species of our group that the neighbourhood contains.

And yet, most emphatically, this is not so. At any time surprises may come along; or, perhaps more accurately, at all times surprises do come along. All naturalists who have retained their enthusiasm for years can corroborate this fact. It is conspicuously true of my own experience. I collected the Arachnida of the Malvern district from 1920 to 1951, and I had my set of favourite haunts—a couple of woods, a hillside, a sunken lane, and a neglected corner of a private estate. They never failed to yield a reward—and my greatest prizes of all turned up in my last two years.

The truth is that although laboratory research can teach us a lot about animals' bodies, it is on our "expeditions" that we get the chance to learn something about animal life. The one thing that can legitimately be said against the use of the Berlese funnel is that it gives us our animals after they have been killed and to this extent justifies the jibe of the field-naturalist who says to the lab-happy anatomist, "You hate to see them alive."

The student of animals must acquire the habit of doing his collecting with his eyes open, and of mixing periods of quiet observation with minutes of intensive acquisition. It is very desirable that he should bring home some definite information about the precise kind of habitat in which this, that and the other species was found, about what is often called its microclimate.

This is one of the kinds of information that ecologists want, and it is also valuable to the collector-student himself. I remember once, on my way up the Malvern Hills, meeting a friend who asked where I was going. I replied that I happened to want a few specimens of a particular species of spider, at which she asked me whether I was sure that I should be able to find them. I was able to assure her that I should (as I did), but this was only because I knew the kind of spot in which to look. Of course all naturalists recognise more or less broadly "a likely place" for the creatures that interest them most, but the more specialised one's study becomes, the more precise should grow one's knowledge of a particular animal's environment.

Hence it is that a "field note-book," to be really used for notes in the fields, not only justifies itself but provides evidence that a collecting expedition is not necessarily just fun. It may be fun, but it can also contribute to biological knowledge.

Chapter V

SMALL ANIMALS: THEIR PRESERVATION

THE preservation of specimens is an essential part of the work of all natural historians and biologists. It is seldom very difficult, but it can easily be done badly or imperfectly, when moth and rust and other more rapidly acting forces of nature destroy one's material with disheartening and even tragic result.

Broadly, the small animals of this book fall into two classes— those whose carcases are hard, dry and nearly imperishable, and those that are soft, juicy and readily decomposable.

Many insects of course belong to the first group, and most entomologists can follow the familiar procedure of the collector of butterflies and set their specimens, impaled on pins, in a way which is too well known to need much description. To the beginner it may be pointed out that more is involved than merely transfixing the body with a pin. The wings must be suitably arranged, and so also, very often, must other organs such as antennae, legs and other appendages, so that they can be readily and clearly seen. A few of each species should be mounted upside down.

The real reason for setting and pinning an insect is not to produce an attractive row of specimens, but to make their examination easier, so that there should be sufficient length of pin to enable the latter to be picked up with forceps and the insect examined from all sides. There must also be room for a label on the same pin. The data on the label should be written on the lower side, so that it is read by turning the whole upside down—an obvious point which many beginners do not realise at first.

All boxes of pinned insects should be protected from damp and should contain a little naphthalene or paradichlorobenzene.

Many, perhaps the majority, of the small animals with which this book is concerned cannot, however, be set and allowed to dry. If they are treated like this their soft bodies shrivel beyond recognition and the skeletal residue looks merely deplorable. Such creatures must be kept in spirit, and many entomologists find in this fact a reason for self-congratulation. Spirit-specimens, they

39

say, are less convenient to handle and are often troublesome to store. This is true only to a limited extent, for a spirit-specimen can be manipulated and examined, sent through the post and generally ill-treated without damage in a way that would reduce a set butterfly to a heap of small fragments.

After a specimen has been identified, it is put, alone or with others, into spirit in a specimen tube. The spirit used should be colourless "industrial" or "surgical" spirit, undiluted, and the tube should be as small as convenient. Two inches by half an inch or a third of an inch is a good average size—larger tubes merely waste space and spirit and are usually more fragile. Every tube should contain a label on which is written the name, date, place of capture and so on. These data can be written in ordinary pencil, which is unaffected by alcohol. I find that the most satisfactory method is to curl the label with the wording outwards round the bottom of the tube and hold it in position with a tight wad of cotton-wool, rammed down with a pencil.

The fundamental difficulty with all spirit-specimens is evaporation, and untold advantages would follow the discovery of a liquid with the preservative properties of alcohol but a much higher boiling-point. The corks that are usually supplied with specimen tubes are sometimes almost useless in preventing evaporation, and although their efficiency is improved by sealing them with paraffin wax the improvement disappears each time that the tube is uncorked and the wax broken. There is really no satisfactory alternative to the long-established method of filling the tube with spirit, closing it with a plug of cotton-wool and inverting it in more spirit in a wide-mouthed bottle. The bottle should have either a very good cork or a ground-glass stopper (Fig. 3). Glass-stoppered bottles are expensive, and if substitutes are used the collection should not be left without inspection for many months.

The number of specimens in a tube, the number of tubes in a bottle and the number of bottles in a collection are matters which are determined by the scale on which the individual naturalist intends to work. It may well be, for example, that a few specimens of the commonest species, contained in a separate tube for each species, will all be kept together in a single bottle, which would thus represent the order as part of a larger collection of animals of several kinds. But many will wish for greater scope than this, and to have a bottle of tubes for each species is not unreasonable;

nor do five or six dozen bottles occupy very much space.

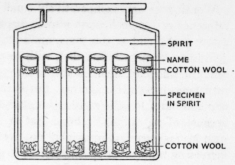

FIG. 3.—The Preservation of Spirit Specimens

Several suggestions may be made concerning this collection of bottles of tubes.

When one begins to collect specimens of any kind of animal one is at first a labourer in a strange vineyard. One's captures are unfamiliar and one suffers from an inevitable distrust in one's early efforts to name them, for one is attempting a task in which the technique is new and the difficulties are unknown. In these circumstances many collectors, as already mentioned, send their specimens to an expert, who names them with an enviable certainty and teaches the collector his job. These specimens form, therefore, a particularly valued part of his collection; they are designated the "authoritatively-named specimens," and as such they should have some distinction. Several methods are possible. Some biologists close the tube with a coloured cork or paint a coloured ring round the outside of the tube-mouth: another very good method is to write the label in Indian ink on coloured paper.

As this stage passes one enters the stage of acquiring a representative collection of the group, until one has a sufficiency of every species from Britain or from Europe or from wherever one's limits are set. This is the main body of the collection: it forms one's own set of "types," specimens which are to be permanently available for reference and comparison. Some biologists like to distinguish foreign from native species by a differently coloured cork or label.

Another category which may not appear in one's collection until later is that of the "figured specimens." These are the individuals which, for one reason or another, have provided material for illustration in a book or a paper: and this fact gives them an added interest and an enhanced value. They should always be clearly distinguishable from the bulk of their less conspicuous and more ordinary brethren.

Working at any comparatively small group brings this main reference or type collection into an approach to completion after a few years, and at this stage one's attitude towards it calls for definition. Some will find that, with smaller chance of the occurrence of a novelty, their interest in the group has waned; and they turn henceforward to another. But if this does not occur, and if one continues to collect either because of the joy of the chase or because of an optimistic hope that at any time a surprise may turn up (as surprises invariably do), what is to be done with the increasing number of specimens? It is pointless, and it may lead to inconvenience, to overload the type collection with disproportionate numbers of the commonest species; and a wise course to adopt is to keep all good, mature, well-marked specimens, which have nothing unusual to distinguish them, in a stock-bottle together. There need be no attempt to separate the different species or the captures of different years, although many will wish to do so. It is surprising how often a stock-bottle of this kind proves itself to be useful. It provides a source from which to accede to requests for specimens, and it supplies a sufficient quantity of material with which to investigate any problem that may crop up in the course of one's own work (as problems invariably do). All good biologists deprecate the mere accumulation of slaughtered unfortunates, and indeed nothing could be more tragically stupid than the row of twenty Death's Head Hawk Moths or the case of a dozen stuffed Kingfishers that sometimes one is called upon to admire; but many small animals belong to a different realm of research; and in practice a well-filled stock-bottle is found to be quite invaluable.

Most of us spend the greater part of our lives in the same place, and the contents of the stock-bottle have therefore generally been provided by one's own neighbourhood. But holidays usually take one elsewhere and the naturalist seizes the opportunity which arises. The stock-bottle method may then be adopted for all unremarkable specimens which the holiday's collecting has produced. The species should be separated into tubes, the tubes included in a bottle in the usual way, and the bottle itself labelled with the locality of its contents and the year of their acquisition.

If a collection of small animals is treated in this way, it becomes a thing of permanent interest and growing value, so that there is little chance of dying enthusiasm.

Finally it should be said that in every collection, and even for single objects which do not form part of a collection, the actual preservation is no more important than the labelling. This point cannot be overemphasised. A specimen without a label has lost if not 100 per cent. at least 90 per cent. of its interest. Its identity may perhaps be obvious enough, but with its label has gone all certain knowledge of when, where and by whom it was found; and these facts add so much to its value that without them it may have lost its claim to being any longer preserved.

It has been my lot on several occasions to be concerned with the arrangement or rearrangement or rescue of the specimens of one museum or another, and, as all who have shared in such work will agree, the usual heart-rending experience is to find large quantities of objects of many kinds with no information at all about their origins.

All museums tend to become repositories for junk, which justifies this expressive description solely because it was never properly labelled. It is a characteristic of the British people that nearly all such valueless objects have come from "east of Suez," and my colleagues and I used comprehensively to designate all these things as "back-scratchers from Borneo"—neither knowing nor caring whether the inhabitants of Borneo do in fact scratch their backs— for it was a wonderfully satisfying term for all shells, fossils, pieces of rock, wood or metal which seemed to have lost their way in the complex labyrinth of civilisation.

The moral of all this is obvious. The natural historian should see to it that his specimens are accurately, fully and permanently labelled. Let him remember that a specimen without a label is about as valuable as a label without a specimen, so that labels must be secured; that a label which reads "23" might as well have been lost with the (invariably missing) catalogue to which it once referred; that a label which says Echinocorys scutata probably tells the reader only what he can see for himself, whereas he wants to know when and where and by whom the specimen was obtained.

Chapter VI

SMALL ANIMALS: THEIR EXAMINATION

SMALL animals can hardly ever be satisfactorily examined while they are alive, simply because they will not keep still. They must be killed and they should always be killed as painlessly as possible. A zoologist above all men should make certain that no animal in his control is subjected to avoidable suffering.

The familiar cyanide bottle almost certainly provides the best method for insects and for many other animals. Its action is not rapid, but it seems to cause no distress. It may be replaced by a similar bottle containing crushed or chopped laurel leaves under a circle of perforated paper by those who have been warned against the use of cyanide, but in fact whatever danger there may be is faced by the maker of the bottle, not by the subsequent user of it.

Another alternative is chloroform; a few drops on a piece of cotton-wool convert an empty bottle into a very lethal chamber. It is a good method for killing sluggish creatures such as earthworms, but the vapour acts as a stimulant to others, which are apt to thrash about and perhaps to injure themselves. The most usual method for such animals is to drown them in spirit, in which they very quickly become insensible.

There is a slight disadvantage with both chloroform and alcohol —the animals sometimes die with their limbs flexed or contracted, and this may make their examination difficult, especially if they are kept in spirit long enough for their muscles to harden. If desired, this may be avoided by dropping the animal into boiling water, which not only kills them in a small fraction of a second but also causes them to die with their legs stretched out. In this position they may be hardened in spirit and are thus preserved in a very convenient attitude.

Human eyes cannot see, unaided, more than a small part of the finer structure of an animal, without a knowledge of which their lives cannot be understood or their identities determined. Hence it is necessary to use either a lens or a combination of lenses, a microscope.

The efficient use of a hand lens does not need much description. There are many kinds on the market, and some of them, more highly priced, are intended to give larger images free from colour and distortion. There must be many who for one reason or another appreciate the help these lenses give, but to those who are constantly working in a biological laboratory where microscopes are always at hand, they are not so necessary. For many purposes, however, a single lens, perhaps $1\frac{1}{4}$ or $1\frac{1}{2}$ inch across and of focal length about 3 inches, is extremely useful both indoors and out. Its diameter assures a large field well illuminated, and its magnifying power is sufficient for much routine work. If it is desired to supplement this, one of the pocket-lenses which consist of three lenses that can be used either separately or together may be recommended.

In use the lens should be held close to the eye and, according to circumstances and convenience, the object raised or the head lowered until the image is focused.

A microscope is, however, essential in all critical biological work; it is needed for thorough examination of nearly all the various parts of small animals, either for information about their structure or in order to name them. In addition, no natural historian can really begin to think of himself as a specialist in the group he has chosen unless his collection is supplemented by an adequate set of slides in which the details of the animals' structure can be clearly seen. For the worker in some groups, false-scorpions, for example, the slide collection is really more important and more useful than the stock of preserved bodies. Hence it is necessary to learn the art of slide-making.

The essence of this process is that the object to be examined, a wing, leg, antenna or other organ, or a portion of some internal tissue, is made translucent and preserved in a suitable adhesive between two pieces of glass. The lower of these, the slide, is by convention usually a 3 inch by 1 inch rectangle; the upper, the cover slip, is very thin and is a circle or a square of any size between $\frac{3}{8}$ inch and $\frac{7}{8}$ inch across.

Many different mountants exist for securing the cover-slip: for the preparation of animal subjects the best are Canada balsam and "Micrex."

For many years, balsam was used almost unhesitatingly for every slide: it is a natural product used in solution in xylol, and the chief point to bear in mind is that anything mounted in it must be quite free from water. If this is not so the object will present a cloudy or misty appearance due to the fact that water and xylol are immiscible.

To remove the water from an object, alcohol is used. Alcohol unites with water so readily that heat is produced, and may distort or destroy the material if it is a delicate tissue. It will not, of course, hurt a robust and naturally almost dry object like a fly's wing or an ant's leg. Therefore the object which has usually been detached or dissected from the animal under water is put first into a watch-glass of 30 per cent. alcohol and left there for a period of three to ten minutes. It is then transferred successively to 50 per cent., 70 per cent., 90 per cent. and "absolute" (100 per cent.) alcohol, remaining for a while in each. The time needed is a matter of judgement and experience and depends on the size, the toughness and the permeability of the object: it is well to remember that many failures are the result of haste over this passage through the alcohols, or upgrading. Apart from waste of time, it cannot be too slow.

A word should be added about absolute alcohol. Really absolute alcohol is very expensive, and in the careless hands of beginners who may breathe on it or sneeze over it does not retain its purity for long. But for all except the highest grades of microscopic work it is unnecessary and its place can be taken by colourless rectified spirit without harm.

When the object has been dehydrated in this way it must be cleared, that is to say freed from alcohol by soaking it in either xylol or oil of cloves, and again this final clearing should not be hurried.

A drop of Canada balsam is then placed on the slide with a glass rod, the object is taken from the clove oil and put into it. It may need some arrangement of its parts, and this is done with a pair of mounted needles. Then the cover-slip is lowered on to it, air bubbles being excluded. Personally, I have never yet been able to resist the temptation to see at once what the preparation looks like, and provided that it is kept horizontal there is no reason why the slide should not be examined immediately under the low power. However, before it can be stored in a box which holds it on its edge, time must be allowed for the balsam to harden. At ordinary temperatures this will take some days, but it may often be accelerated by gentle warmth.

In the use of micrex, beginners usually achieve very good results more easily. The object to be mounted is transferred from 70 per cent. alcohol to "cellosolve," a trade name for diethylene glycol, thence to xylol and is then mounted in micrex. There is not the same necessity for the removal of the last trace of water; moreover, micrex does not turn yellow with age as Canada balsam does. In fact the introduction of the cellosolve-micrex technique is a boon to beginners—and others.

Many objects are greatly improved by staining before being mounted. This not only makes them more conspicuous, but also helps to distinguish different components from each other, since they will absorb the dye at different rates and thus show contrasting shades. In fact, nearly all soft tissues are stained as a matter of course.

One of the best general stains for animal matter is borax carmine. This is dissolved in 70 per cent. alcohol and the object, after it has reached alcohol of this strength, is put into the stain for one, two or three minutes. It is then washed in more 70 per cent. alcohol and then mounted in the usual way.

Even better results are obtained by using two contrasting stains, the commonest pair for general purposes being eosin and haematoxylin. Both may be used dissolved in alcohol. The object is stained with eosin, washed in 70 per cent. alcohol, stained with haematoxylin, and put into 70 per cent. alcohol to which a few drops of ammonia have been added. This turns the haematoxylin blue, so that it contrasts well with the red of the eosin. The mounting of the object is then completed.

It will be seen that the process of ordinary slide-making is not an elaborate one; it is in fact easily mastered and it is very fascinating. Nor is it necessary to have an elaborately equipped laboratory in which to carry it out. This is an important consideration, especially for younger naturalists who may have to conduct all the operations involved in their hobby in a part of their bedrooms. The young chemist is notoriously constrained or frustrated in his efforts to continue his experiments at home, and it is not impossible to find sympathy with those who modify the encouragement they offer; but the young biologist is well served by a plain table set under a window, while a shelf or two in a cup-

board will hold all his necessary bottles, apparatus and specimens. He does not need nearly as much accommodation or equipment as a comparably enthusiastic and efficient photographer.

Certain general observations may be given to round off the subject of microscope slide-making. First, too much emphasis cannot
be laid on reasonable cleanliness. Slides and cover-slips should be
quite clean before they are used, and xylol is the best liquid with
which to wash them. But some people are not reasonable about
this, and the beginner may well be warned against unnecessarily
adopting the attitude that slides and cover-slips must always be
stored in a stoppered bottle of xylol, that they must never be
touched except with forceps and that they must never be wiped
except with a special kind of soft paper. It may be granted that
there are circumstances in which this kind of behaviour is advis-
able, but it is only common sense to wait for them before becoming a crank.

These remarks do not apply with the same force to the microscope itself, which cannot be given too much respect. Its greatest
enemy is dust, and every precaution should be taken to prevent
the entry of dust particles both into the microscope and into its
case, and the instrument should never be left exposed when it is
not being used. But the microscope itself is really the young
biologist's biggest problem. It is a valuable and an expensive
thing; and it is not usually regarded as an essential part of the
equipment of a home, where the motor-car, the wireless set, the
refrigerator and the telephone are all given priority over it, and
rated as necessities. The naturalist therefore faces one of those
obstacles, and there are many like it in life, which disappear when
money is available, but in no other way. The only solution of the
difficulty is to make use of the microscopes in the school biological
laboratory, and permission to do this at convenient times can be
sought only from the biology teacher in charge. This book can
offer no advice on the method of approach!

When, by some means or another, a microscope has been made
accessible, two points should be mentioned.

Do not, in the first place, be too ready to assume that you can
by instinct use it and treat it in the best way. Half an hour's advice
and instruction from an experienced microscopist, or an intelligent
use of one of the many books which tell you what to do and what
not to do, will be certainly repaid.

A woodlouse.

Common earwig newly
emerged.

A silver-fish
(*Lepisma*).

Secondly, do not think that a microscope does not justify its existence unless it is giving you a magnification of some five hundred diameters upwards. The use of the "high power" objective, focal length 4 mm., should not be regarded as the normal routine for any and every slide. It is indeed a fact, which only experience can confirm, that the lower powers often teach the observer most, and I personally strongly recommend preliminary examination with as long a focal length as an inch. A one-inch objective gives the beginner ample magnifying power, as well as more light and a greater space between slide and lens; hence it helps to avoid accidents.

This objective is also especially valuable for the examination of entire animals. Many of these are examined directly, without being mounted, in the process of discovering their identities, and if they are spirit-specimens they are often scrutinised while lying in spirit in a watch-glass or small white saucer. They need direct illumination from above, or from the side, for which nothing is better than bright sunlight. This examination in spirit is often inconvenient, and it is a fact not always realised that specimens are seldom harmed if allowed to dry for an hour or two.

Finally, there is a feature which microscope slides share with books. As all scholars and book-lovers know, the books that one possesses tend to multiply at such a rate that one can almost believe that they have powers of reproduction. In this respect they are certainly equalled and often surpassed by one's collection of slides, which accumulate at an incredible speed. They are so easy and so satisfying to make, and so attractive to look at; they are cheaper than books and are neither as heavy nor as bulky, yet even so their storage soon raises a problem in the laboratory.

There is only one way in which this difficulty can be partially solved. It seems to be a tradition among many microscopists, especially the professionals in the trade, that a slide can never carry more than one object or, at least, more than one cover-slip. Since the area of a slide is ten or twelve times that of the cover-slip, this is manifestly untrue. There is no reason at all why a cover-slip should not cover more than one object, nor why a slide should not carry two or even three cover-slips, and if this practice is adopted (Fig. 4), the number of finished slides demanding storage-space can be very considerably reduced.

Lastly, it may be added that all that has been written above

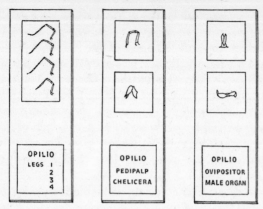

FIG. 4.—An Arrangement of Eight Organs on Three Slides

about the labelling of specimens applies with equal force to the labelling of slides. Moreover, the label should be written and fixed as soon as the slide has been found on examination to be worth keeping. In a zoological laboratory well known to me in my youth there was displayed a conspicuously printed message in these words—"Label it to-day; for to-morrow you will have forgotten." There is no need to emphasise the truth of this.

A small detail about labelling which is often forgotten is that additional information and comments may be written on a second label, which is stuck on the lower side of the glass, underneath the first one.

Chapter VII

SMALL ANIMALS: THEIR IDENTIFICATION

WHEN our small animals have been found, caught, preserved and examined it is essential to discover their names. Until a specimen has been identified it is impossible either to tell our colleagues what we have done, or to find out what other students have already written about it; and although there is often a temptation to believe that as soon as we are able to give a name to any animal which we have caught we have done all that is necessary, it is yet quite certain that an animal unnamed is almost wholly valueless. We cannot read about it, we cannot helpfully compare it with its relatives, and we cannot, for very long, continue to call it "that queer one we found on Friday." We must learn the task of identification.

The naming of species is a problem that differs considerably among the various groups. Some are relatively easy to determine, like harvestmen; others are very much harder, like centipedes. It is here that the help of the expert is of the greatest value, enabling the beginner to detect the mistakes he has very possibly made, or, more encouraging, confirming him in his beliefs when he is correct.

The beginner, we may suppose, is working from a printed "key," or only from a series of separate descriptions of species. He cannot, at first, be sure that he has rightly grasped the significance either of what he sees in the specimen before him or what he reads on the pages of his book; and at this stage he is uncertain as to whether he is right or wrong in his conclusions. He has no alternative to asking the opinion of someone who knows.

It is only fair to point out that experts, as is natural, do not all respond with the same readiness to appeals for identification of specimens, nor is there any reason why they should do so. Some are busy men, some are men of leisure. Some return the specimens, with their names, immediately or within a week; some keep them for a month and some do not reply at all. Some again, it is reported, respond with a printed circular, saying that their fee for identification is half-a-guinea a specimen, which seems good value for an animal like Phalangium opilio or Orchesella cincta. The writer must, however, admit that he has never yet encountered one of this professional band, and that arachnologists in particular seem to be a particularly courteous and charitable band of biologists; but the mere existence of the rumour does emphasise the fact that the beginner has no right to demand help, and that he should assure himself that he is not asking for time that his helper can ill spare from more important work.

For if authorities differ, so also do students. Some of them write with full awareness of what they are asking, and respond with appreciation of the help or information they may receive. Others do not; and to find included in the day's correspondence, as the writer once found, a box of thirty tubes of preserved spiders, accompanied by a scrap of paper bearing the words, "Kindly name the enclosed," is not perhaps the most tactful way of seeking the assistance that is required. A little consideration and forbearance will often go a long way.

The task of discovering by oneself the name of any particular species that one has caught is made easier by the use of a scheme known to biologists as a "dichotomic key." Keys of this sort are often found in botanical books, for our knowledge of the species of plants is more complete than our knowledge of the much larger number of species of animals; and keys are becoming more customary in natural history books, for they are also a very good way of displaying the characteristics and the differences of any group of objects. The clearest, most obvious way to display distinguishing characteristics is of course on a chart composed of parallel columns suitably headed, and here is a simple example which might have been made to distinguish four common animals, bird, dog, frog, wasp, for anyone who was not familiar with them.

WITH WINGS		WITHOUT WINGS	
WITH 2 LEGS	WITH 6 LEGS	WITH HAIR	WITHOUT HAIR
BIRD	WASP	DOG	FROG

When the number of separate items is small, charts are easy to produce and use; when the number is more than ten or a dozen, a chart suffers from the practical disadvantage that it cannot be printed on an ordinary page, and the insertion of special "throw-out" pages is expensive. But it should be emphasised that the naturalist will learn a great deal about his group of animals if he gets some large sheets of paper and rules up charts for his own benefit.

Although in theory keys should be foolproof, they are not altogether easy to use without some practice—in fact a cynic has said that keys are only helpful to anyone who knows all the species beforehand. To give some instruction in the use of a key, the same animals are here placed in one:

1(2) With wings		3
2(1) Without wings		5
3(4) With two legs		BIRD
4(3) With six legs		WASP
5(6) With hair		DOG
6(5) Without hair		FROG

This shows that the puzzled naturalist should look first to see if his specimen possesses wings. If it has he then reads line 3, if it has not he reads line 5. Line 3 and its alternative 4 tell him to count its legs and so to distinguish a bird with two legs from a wasp with six; line 5 and its alternative 6 tell him to look for hair, which a dog has and a frog has not.

Although this key is so simple as to be ludicrous, it shows perfectly the form and use of a key. It may be noted here that the same animals might be separated by the use of a wholly different set of characteristics, thus:

1(2) With a sting		WASP
2(1) Without a sting		3
3(4) With feathers		BIRD
4(3) Without feathers		5
5(6) With warm blood . . .		DOG
6(5) With cold blood		FROG

If this key is examined, it will be seen that it would not be so satisfactory in use as the first one. A wasp which had an ovipositor instead of a sting would be identified as a frog; a nestling without feathers would turn out to be a dog; and a dead dog whose blood was cold would be indeterminable. The point of this is that in constructing keys—and most specialists are called upon to do so at some time—the most useful characters must be carefully chosen.

It should further be noticed that the same characteristics of the same animals can be "keyed" in different ways. Thus the first key given above might have read thus:

1(4)	Without wings	.	.	.	2
2(3)	Without hair	.	.	.	FROG
3(2)	With hair .	.	.	.	DOG
4(1)	With wings .	.	.	.	5
5(6)	With two legs	.	.	.	BIRD
6(5)	With six legs	.	.	.	WASP

In all these keys each line has its own number and is the alternative to the line whose number follows it in parenthesis. But other methods of construction have been practised, and two of the commonest are illustrated here:

1	With wings	.	2	1	With wings	.	2
1′	Without wings .		3	„	Without wings .		3
2	With two legs	.	BIRD	2	With two legs	.	BIRD
2′	With six legs	.	WASP	„	With six legs	.	WASP
3	With hair .	.	DOG	3	With hair .	.	DOG
3′	Without hair	.	FROG	„	Without hair	.	FROG

It only remains to be said that keys for all groups of animals are not yet in existence and therefore cannot be found: also that any naturalist who has a known species included in a strange key will find it extraordinarily valuable to work through the key backwards. There is no better way of getting to know the organs or other characteristics on which classification is based, or of becoming aware of the difficulties in detecting them.

As has been said, keys are seldom foolproof, however much care has been taken in trying to make them so, but there is another feature about them which should be mentioned. This is that many keys exist which are confessedly limited in scope—they include, perhaps, the "common" species only, or the "large" species only, or the species of a particular area only. For example, the keys in this book are all limited to the species so far recorded in Great Britain. It follows, therefore, that any such key may be used with apparently perfect accuracy and may yet fail to reveal the identity of a given specimen or may give it a name which is not really its own. For example, the illustrative key given in this chapter would cause its user to believe (in the absence of other knowledge) that a cat was a dog.

This kind of mistake can be avoided if, after the use of the key and the discovery of the probable identity, the specimen is carefully compared, step by step, phrase by phrase, with the full printed description of the species which the larger works of reference contain. On the care with which this is done, and on the care with which the description has been written, depend the naturalist's chance of knowing when he has found a strange species, which may be new to his locality or new to Britain, or even new to science.

Yet, with all this discussion of dichotomic keys and long authoritative descriptions, every naturalist knows that there is a much easier way to determine the name of an animal. I do not suppose that anyone who had caught a butterfly which is new to him would think of working through a key in order to run down its name. He would take the best illustrated book on butterflies that was available and turn over its coloured plates until he came to the picture of his capture. His problem would then be immediately solved.

This is the practical way to do the job, but of course it is possible only with well-known objects, like butterflies, moths, seashells, birds' eggs and wild flowers, which are popular and attractive things to study and about which there is therefore an extensive popular literature. There are very few books about the superficially less fascinating small animals of this book which are illustrated with coloured plates.

And, of course, the method is one that suits the collector who is satisfied as soon as his specimen is named, but it does not introduce the student to the structure of the animal or the principles of classification. That is why examining bodies who expect candidates to be able to use a Flora for naming a plant forbid the use of a Flora composed of illustrations only. But even so, whenever good illustrations are accessible it is not a method to be neglected; on the contrary, it is the obvious thing to do first. It makes the rest of the task very much easier, because even if it does not supply the answer at once, it often puts one on the right track.

In the course of a year I am usually asked to name a fair number of spiders, not always British, and if, after consulting such books and papers as I have in my own possession, I am defeated, I take the specimen to the Natural History Museum at South Kensington, select the most likely volume and start by looking at the pictures. This may be "low-brow" arachnology, but it is certainly common sense.

Chapter VIII

SMALL ANIMALS: THEIR DISTRIBUTION

THE distribution of any animal or group of animals forms, if one may so put it, a kind of background or setting to the whole study of Zoology. The subject of our investigation, whatever it may be, lives its life within a certain area of the earth's surface to the exclusion of the rest—it is "here" and not "there." Such a statement at once invites the question, Why is this so? and it is one of the tasks of the zoologist first to ascertain the facts and then to determine if possible the nature of the limiting factors which confine an animal to a restricted space, or which dot it sporadically in separated colonies over a wide area, or which release it to spread itself over a country, a continent or a world.

The matter has two separate aspects, each capable of treatment in two complementary ways. The first is the plain geographical problem—to discover, given an area such as Worcestershire or Wales, what species of our chosen group live therein; or alternatively to determine, given a species, where it lives and where the limits of its domain are set. The completion of this task can be achieved by a sufficiency of what may be called "mere collecting," or a prolonged gathering of all specimens obtainable, as if the accumulation of their bodies were an end in itself.

When the results of such work are set out in tabular form, with the names of the animals along one margin and the names of the countries, counties or parishes along the other, the complementary sides of the question are of course simultaneously displayed. For example, from a table such as the one given on page 58 it is possible to see at once which species of the genus D—— are known to have been found in Worcestershire, and from which counties the species D. magnus has been recorded, and so on.

One of the tasks which soon confronts a naturalist who adopts as "his own" any one of these groups of small animals in the way this book suggests will be to compile a table like this one for his own note-book. He will gradually fill it from his own collecting, at home and on holidays, and from his reading of the

	D. magnus	D. minor	D. niger	D. virescens	D. tristis	D. smithi	etc.
Bedfordshire .	x	x		x			
Berkshire .			x		x	x	
Buckinghamshire	x			x			
etc. to							
Wiltshire . .	x						
Worcestershire	x	x	x		x	x	
Yorkshire .	x			x			

records of others. The search for these records, appearing, as they so often do, inconspicuously in the pages of obscure local journals, provides much pleasure, and gives much valuable information about the attention that his animals have already attracted.

The second aspect of distribution is the ecological aspect, concerned with the relation between the various species and the kinds of haunts or habitats in which they live. To this, again, there are two sides—to determine, given a type of habitat such as a ditch, a mountain-top or a cave, what species live in it; or alternatively to determine, given a species, in what kind of habitat, or microclimate, it is to be found in different parts of the country and at different times of the year. It is clear that the discussion of these problems requires more careful collecting and more acute observation and patient recording of data, often on the spot, than does the uncritical collecting of simple zoo-geography. In consequence, less is known about it, although more may be learnt from it about the lives of all animals and plants.

In consequence, also, it is much more worth while. It gives a point to one's continuing study of animals out of doors after one's actual collection of species is reasonably complete: it forces one to ask oneself, of each species encountered, Why is it here? and what is the part it is playing in this community?

The important features in the environment of any animal may be divided into an organic group and an inorganic group. The former includes the supply of living food, the presence of mates, the existence of enemies in the shape of predators and parasites, and the nature of the vegetation and the shelter it provides; the latter includes all such physical conditions as temperature, humidity, wind-velocity, illumination and the changes to which these factors are liable, as well as the chemical composition of the soil, the water and the air.

Animals react conspicuously to changes in all these details of their environments, so that they move themselves, either by conscious and purposive actions or by mechanical reflex responses, into an environment or a "niche" with which their bodies are in equilibrium. Thus there is a constant relation between an organism and its surroundings, which may be compared to the relation between a key and a lock. The key represents the organism, the lock the surroundings, and each ward a particular physical condition. If the key fits and turns in the lock, the animal lives and reproduces in its environment. If a ward is altered the key can no longer turn, but a different key may do so.

Temperature has a direct effect on the lives of invertebrates. This is to be expected since the body of a cold-blooded animal is more or less at the same temperature as the air surrounding it and temperature determines the rate of its movements and of many of its internal activities. Many small animals seem to be adapted to particular temperatures and to avoid any considerable deviation from what may be considered as their optimum. It is, in fact, a feature that is characteristic of many animals and of a variety of physical conditions that the actual value of the temperature, pressure, humidity or other condition is not as important as the changes to which that condition may be subject. For example, the underside of a stone or a piece of wood is often thickly populated with a gathering of creatures sheltering there. To us, perhaps, a stone may not seem to represent a particularly efficient form of shelter, but measurements can be made to test this. Thus, in 1924 Major R. W. G. Hingston recorded the maximum and minimum temperatures in the air and beneath a stone on the slopes of Everest, at a height of 17,000 feet. His results were as follows:

	In the air	Under stone
Maximum . .	56° F.	39°
Minimum . .	12°	27°
Range . . .	44°	12°

Observations of this kind, made with maximum and minimum thermometers, could be repeated without much difficulty by many naturalists, and the results would be of interest and value to themselves and to other biologists.

Light, too, has an unsuspectedly great effect upon invertebrate life. It appears to be generally true that light falling on the eyes of an animal produces photo-chemical changes in the neighbourhood of the retina and that the compounds thus produced have considerable effect on the metabolism of the animal. This is probably the ultimate cause of the fact that so many invertebrates appear to prefer darkness, a type of behaviour which is discussed more fully in the next chapter. A very good example of the effect of light is seen when nocturnal animals with large eyes, like moths, are subjected to very bright illumination. The result is such a strain on the nervous system that the creature may for a time become almost rigid, until the light is removed and it has had an opportunity to recover.

If it be accepted that light has this disturbing kind of effect on animals, it is easy to understand how they tend to avoid it. Further, it may be remembered that the illumination of an animal is a condition that is constantly changing; normally it changes continuously throughout the hours from sunrise to sunset, so that it may vary between absolute darkness and the full glare of the midday sun. In this it is in marked contrast to gravity, which also affects an animal's movements, but which is always the same both in force and in direction.

Water vapour is particularly important to small animals, many of which suffer discomfort, or at least lose their efficiency and soon die, if they are kept in too dry an atmosphere.

All students of elementary physics are familiar with the description of evaporation in terms of escaping molecules and are aware of the distinction between saturated and unsaturated vapours. But for the animal the problem involves a slight extension of these ideas. Of course in saturated water vapour its body will lose no moisture, but if the relative humidity is, say, 50 per cent., it will do so. Yet the temperature also has an effect. A litre of air containing water vapour at a relative humidity of 50 per cent. and a temperature of 5° C. cannot take up as great a weight of water as a similar litre at 15° C. Hence more important than the relative humidity is the saturation deficiency, measured as the quantity of water absorbable.

Further, water does not evaporate in still air as rapidly as in air that is in motion, even if it has the same saturation deficiency, so that for the animal the most important factor of all is the evaporating power of the air, a consequence of saturation deficiency and movement, measured as the quantity of water taken up as vapour per unit of time.

Lastly it should be repeated that in general an invertebrate animal seems to be less affected by any particular circumstance than by a change in circumstances. Both species as a whole and individuals themselves may become tolerant of high or low temperatures, or of high or low humidities, and may rest in equilibrium with surrounding conditions, but a fall of temperature, to choose an example which is especially effective, quickly upsets this state of rest and the animal begins to move about, or to behave as if it were seeking the old conditions.

The foregoing paragraphs attempt to show that different physical conditions have a considerable effect on the lives of small invertebrates, and especially that a change in the condition is of greater importance than the actual condition itself. The result of the interplay of all these shifting circumstances is seen in the varying numbers of specimens of a particular species which may be found in different localities at the same time, and more particularly in the same locality at different times.

The question of animal numbers, or of the changes in population-density from year to year, is a large one, applicable to animals of every kind. Anyone who has carried on his collecting in the same woods and fields during a number of years will know that some years are good and others are bad, either for a group as a whole or sometimes for one or more species in particular. This is the collector's impression of fluctuating numbers, which is an important part of ecology. One example, taken from my own experience, may perhaps be justified.

In 1890 the only harvestman recorded from Hertfordshire was Lacinius ephippiatus, and fifty years later this species was still the sole published record for the county. Believing this to be an inadequate representation of the fauna, I took the opportunity, on 10 August, 1942, of a visit to the county to try to improve it. I chose a spot well-known to me from my youth, Gravel Lane, close to the southern edge of the Aldenham cricket field, searched the hedges and ditches for a few hours, and returned with examples of eleven different species. This was as much as, if not more than, might have been expected, but it seemed to show that Gravel Lane was a "good place," and in August 1947 I returned in the hope of increasing the list. Search for an hour and a half failed to reveal a single specimen of any species.

The year 1947 was notorious in more ways than one, and in Worcestershire the change in animal population was most conspicuous. The memorable frosts of the early months of the year— in Malvern it snowed on the fiftieth day of the infliction—was followed by extensive flooding, a habit to which the Severn has always been inclined at the smallest provocation, and this in turn was followed by a hot, dry summer. Nearly all my favourite collecting grounds were barren, or, as my former colleague used tersely to remark as we beat and sifted in vain, "Azooic; but negative information is always valuable."

The excuse for this anecdote is that it illustrates the point of view of the ecologist. He always wants to know not only what species are present in or absent from a given environment, niche or micro-climate, but also why they are there, or not there, and why other species are to be expected, or not. There is still a large amount of observational work to be done, recording the facts of dispersal in areas of different characters.

Chapter IX

SMALL ANIMALS: THEIR BEHAVIOUR

A SERIOUS investigator of any group of animals very soon begins to bring back his captures alive, to discover how they may be kept alive in suitable cages and to observe their habits when in captivity. This is not always quite as simple as it seems if it is to be done successfully. An animal that is dropped into an empty box, supplied with a piece of possibly unsuitable food and thus allowed to drag out the rest of its life until death releases it, is the subject of an atrocity of which no biologist should be guilty. It will certainly teach him nothing.

It is therefore necessary to determine the conditions in which small animals can live satisfactorily, and it is soon found that these are not the same for all, nor are they even the same for different kinds of the same creature. There are, indeed, a few that appear to ask for little consideration and are therefore the easiest to accommodate. In many cases a jam-pot seems to be all that is wanted to meet their needs. It may be improved by the addition of a sandy or earthy bottom, and of a stone or two for shelter. Many animals are unable to climb the glass sides, and for these the jars need not even be covered: climbers can be retained by a sheet of glass, a disc of cardboard or a piece of cellophane held down by a rubber band. Better results can often be obtained by using enamel pie-dishes instead of jam-pots. They are shallower so that the animals are more visible and more accessible.

In general, however, cages are most satisfactorily made from cardboard boxes with glass, perspex or cellophane tops. The box should always contain some kind of shelter, for few animals are comfortable in continuous light; some stones or a folded piece of paper fastened into one corner will provide shade and will make a surprising difference to the efficiency of the cage.

Animals that more earnestly seek darkness may have burrows provided for them, made from rolls of paper or rolls of corrugated cardboard. Again, cages sometimes fail to make animals comfortable because the floor and sides are too smooth, and it is then a wise plan to line them with fine glass-paper. This offers a rough surface more nearly resembling the sandy surroundings to which the animal may be accustomed.

The rule in cage-making should be to aim at some passable imitation of the conditions of nature. If the results of our observations and experiments are to lay any claim to trustworthiness, the circumstances of the animals should be as natural as possible. An experiment in biology is an observation made under controlled conditions, and usually these conditions are an important feature and have a great bearing on the results.

For example, a condition which it is very easy to overlook is the dampness of the atmosphere. Many small animals are unable to survive for more than a few hours in dry air, and others are closely dependent on a certain degree of humidity according to the temperature. Some animals must have water they can drink; others do not drink, and so on.

There is little reason to doubt that small invertebrates suffer less from the mere fact of captivity than do many other animals with keener senses, a fuller consciousness of events and a greater dependence on unrestricted freedom. Very probably they do not suffer at all, but are rather fortunate in finding themselves provided with food and free from the attacks of enemies.

By far the most obvious characteristic common to woodlice, earwigs, ants and scorpions is that during part of their lives they are all actively or even busily engaged in doing something. It is this that makes animals for many people more interesting than plants, for in the things they do animals often show remarkable differences from the things we do ourselves.

The actions of animals therefore provide the raw material of the science of Animal Behaviour, and if there is anything of which the readers of this book can be quite certain it is that they will be able, if they wish, to find many opportunities of making additions to the recorded facts on which this branch of biology is based. The observation of behaviour is seldom very difficult; animals themselves provide countless opportunities and the biologist has only to find the time and patience. The difficulties come later.

These difficulties are of two kinds: those of reporting or describing the facts observed and those of interpreting these facts. Students of animal behaviour are, clearly, asking two kinds of questions, the first, How do animals behave? and the second, Why do animals so behave?

Earwigs,
male and female.

Earwig with wings expanded.

Female cockroach with her egg-case.

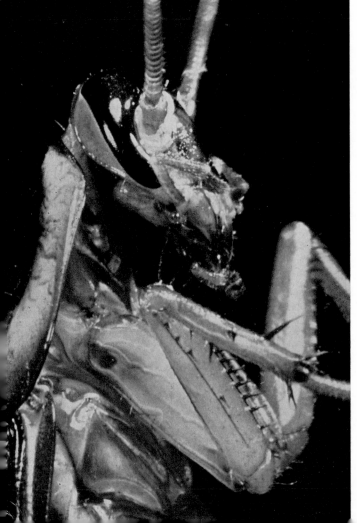

Head of a cockroach at extremely close range.

Biologists differ among themselves in choosing the words that may be used in describing an animal's actions. Some assume without question that the animals are in some way aware of what they are doing, that they are consciously striving to attain an end and to achieve a purpose in the same sort of way as does a human being. An example of a description on these lines of a scene that can easily be imagined by the reader would be: "The creature, frightened by the appearance of its enemy, tried to save itself by hiding under a stone."

It is to be observed that in this apparently innocent sentence the following assumptions have been made:

    i that the creature was frightened;
   ii that it was frightened by what it saw;
  iii that it recognised what it saw as an enemy;
  iv that it tried to hide itself from its enemy;
   v that its intention in hiding was to save itself from injury or death.

All these assumptions themselves presuppose the existence of a mind in the animal and suppose further that conscious processes occurring in that mind are like enough to those in a human mind to be described in the same terms.

An alternative description of the same event would be: "When the predatory species approached the other, the latter moved closer to the stone."

This is the kind of description that would be given by a more cautious observer; it is no more than a verifiable statement of fact and makes no assumption of any mental state, or even of the existence of awareness at all. Some biologists would approve of this sort of description; others would say that it errs in being ultra-cautious and seems to suggest that the animal is no more, or not much more, than a machine. It is not at all easy to decide which of the two methods of description is to be accepted while the other is to be abandoned. The former is the more picturesque, it is more suggestive to a reader and it emphasises the fact that the animal is alive and that its survival depends on its responses. The latter is coldly inhuman and has a spurious air of simplicity about it which is, perhaps, superficially attractive, but which often fails to carry conviction.

It is well worth while to push the discussion of these two points of view a stage further, in order to show the experimental naturalist some of the difficulties he may meet.

The first point, which is indeed obvious, is the impossibility of knowing what mental processes, if any, are going on inside the animal, or to put it more simply, what the animal is thinking. He would be a bold man who would venture to say what thoughts were passing through the mind of his best friend at any particular moment, and when for the friend there is substituted an earwig, a centipede or a slug the difficulty becomes insuperable. Many of the actions that an animal undertakes are customarily described as instinctive, and one of the most conspicuous features of instinctive actions is that they often show a rigid adherence to routine in which, however often they may be performed, no modification is made. Stimulus and response are so inseparably connected that no alteration or improvement is possible. But modification of response is the only evidence an animal gives us that its responses are in fact conscious ones; a mere reaction may be no more a conscious act than is the closing of the iris of the eye in a bright light.

The assumption of a conscious state in an animal during its responses can be only our own interpretation of its movements. But since movement alone is not evidence of consciousness, it is often difficult not to misinterpret it. An instance of this occurred to me recently and is so good an illustration of the point that it may be narrated here.

I was standing one August evening at the side of one of the ponds in the Jardin des Tuileries where a number of youthful Parisians were sailing model yachts and toy boats. Presently a small boat came sailing across the water and pushed its tiny bowsprit against the concrete ledge at my feet. It was apparently deserted by its owner, for it was unclaimed, and remained for some moments repeatedly ramming the unscaleable stonework, hitting it and rebounding from it, first on one tack, then on the other. Of a sudden there must have been a change of wind. The little vessel backed, turned round and sailed away, heeling over to the breeze, to strike the shore again not far from where I stood, and to be instantly picked up by its possessor.

The whole of this little scene bore to an imaginative observer every sign of purposive action. The repeated attempts to leave the water at my feet, the attack on the concrete by different methods of approach, the final disappointed abandonment and the joyful race across the pond to the one person in all the crowd who would lift it up and care for it—all this was plain to see. *And it was all nonsense.* There is neither a biologist nor a yachtsman in the world who would agree that the toy boat was trying to find someone to take it out of the water, but *it looked exactly as if it were.*

Now animals respond to wind-pressures as do boats, and also to temperature changes, to scents, to vibrations, to moisture and to other circumstances with exactly the same appearance of a purposiveness they may be very far from feeling. The lesson we learn is that we cannot be too cautious in describing what we have seen.

But granting this, as many will, we come very soon to the fact that competent observers, familiar with the ways of the animals they are watching, have found it impossible to avoid the use of psychological terms, implying the existence of purposive efforts. We read, for instance, of a wasp which, trying to fly away with a paralysed insect, apparently discovered that the wings, catching the air, made too great a resistance; whereupon it stopped, bit off the wings and resumed its flight. We read of insects on the march building a bridge or a dam across a stream and of one of their number which got into the water to hold a particular stone in place against the force of the current until further building progress made this extra support unnecessary. We read of the language of bees, or the peculiar dance-movements by which they convey information to one another: it has even been said that it is easier to understand the speech of bees than that of some races of the human species.

Thus it can be seen that both the recording and the interpretation of animal behaviour present difficulties of their own and the best advice that can be given to the individual biologist is that he should decide which "school of thought" claims his appreciation and that he should then study its principles and try to apply its rules consistently in all the records and notes that he writes.

The actions of animals are often divided, more by convention than by any natural diversity, into a number of different categories. These may be called reflex actions, tropistic actions and instinctive actions, and something may be said about each.

Simple responses to direct stimuli from without are often of the type known as reflex actions. They are usually immediate, automatic in the sense that they do not have to be learnt, and all members of a species show them in the same circumstances. An example in human beings is the opening and closing of the iris in the front of the eye. This occurs as a result of the intensity of the light falling on it; it is quite unconscious and quite beyond voluntary control. Since all established reflexes are directed towards the well-being of the animal, they often give it a very purposive appearance, and an animal or even a recently severed part of an animal may perform a series of reflex actions and seem to an observer to be as full of intention as did the sailing-boat.

Very often reflexes cause an animal to turn its body into a particular direction, and then to move towards or away from the source of the stimulus. Thus a moth flies into the flame of a candle because, it may be, the light that falls on its eyes produces effects which are transmitted from the cells of the retinas to the muscles of the wings. The more brightly illuminated eye causes a slower beating of the wings on the same side, so that the insect is turned about until the eyes are equally illuminated and the wings in consequence beat equally powerfully. It must now fly towards the flame, going not where it wishes to go but where its wings carry it.

These turning movements or directed reflexes are called tropisms, and both animals and plants show tropistic responses of this kind to light, gravity, water, air or fluid pressure on their flanks and to several other external sources of stimulation also.

Kineses are movements of an animal in directions determined by a changing intensity of some external condition. For example, it may go from dry air to moist air, from cold air to warm air, or vice versa, as if it were uncomfortable in one and comfortable in the other. Comfort is too human a word to use in this way, for it suggests a conscious appreciation of the particular circumstances; and it may be wiser to suggest that an animal's body-tissues are in equilibrium with one set of physical conditions and not with the other. When moths fly to "sugar" at night and wasps fly into the marmalade at breakfast their movements are of this kind and it is a better way to describe them than the too simple suggestion that wasps like marmalade.

Most people would describe the actions of animals as being due to "instinct," but would not be so ready to define the word or to explain what instinct is. Instinctive actions are movements which are innate or unlearned, are often complex, like the spinning of a spider's web, and are often carried out as if they were under the tyranny of an unreasoning impulse, forcing the animal to act in a particular way. Moreover, unlike reflexes and tropisms, instinctive actions are often directed towards a distant goal and their value may become apparent some months later, when some event has occurred, which can have had no influence on the animal but which by its instinctive actions was preparing for it.

It is customary nowadays to suppose that an "internal releasing mechanism" sets a series of actions going when it meets the appropriate "sign stimulus," and much investigation to-day is directed to describing the sign stimuli for particular actions. For example, young herring-gulls lift their opened beaks when they are about to be fed, and the sign stimulus appears to be the pink spot on the beak of the parent bird. Young birds often react in the same way to a pink patch or even to any contrasting patch on an object which only remotely resembles a gull's head.

Much of this work on instinctive response to sign stimuli is based on the behaviour of birds and fishes. There is no reason at present to believe that the instinctive behaviour of ants and wood-lice is different in essence; and the opportunities for interesting original work in this direction are wide open to all who appreciate the advantages of "small animals."

It will be noticed that this view of instinctive behaviour is more mechanistic in character than generous to the "mind" of the animal. To some extent this kind of interpretation of behaviour is suited to a mechanical age, and is reflected even in the opinions of those concerned with the behaviour of other human beings. The criminal is regarded less as a responsible person who has deliberately chosen an anti-social way of life and rendered himself liable to well-deserved punishment, but more and more as a "young delinquent" who was unfortunately misdirected and deserves psychiatry and sympathy to cure him of his trouble.

On the other hand, so experienced an observer of ants as D. Wragge Morley records that there are to be found in nests both energetic ants and lazy ants, both of which are capable of setting an example and inspiring or infecting their companions. The reader may be inclined to agree; he has known, he says, clever dogs and stupid dogs; may there not equally be clever centipedes and stupid centipedes, wise earwigs and foolish earwigs? Ethology, the scientific study of animal behaviour, is not as yet prepared to supply an unqualified answer, but the young naturalist historian can certainly look for evidence which may help to do so.

Chapter X

SMALL ANIMALS: THEIR LITERATURE

SIDE by side with his collecting, dissecting and observing, the naturalist must aim at acquiring some familiarity with the existing literature of his chosen group. Here once more the contrast between the ornithologist and the specialist in an order of small animals is remarkable. The former will find waiting for him in almost every bookshop a large selection of recent books, with many beautiful coloured plates and many admirable photographs, often the result of a bird-watcher's patient enthusiasm and technical skill. He can make his choice from a range which leads from such works as *Our Feathered Friends of the Hedgerow* through authoritative and almost miraculously cheap Pelican books to a many-volumed *Handbook of British Birds* and even to rare works, prized by collectors of fine books because of their artistic merit, which will cost him a large portion of a month's salary. The latter will find no such masses of available guidance—a fact which is in itself an incentive to enthusiastic study, for it emphasises how little is already known. The larger "Natural Histories" will contain references to his group, longer or shorter according to their scope and more or less inaccurate according to their ages and the character of their editors and authors. In any case, there may well be difficulties about consulting any such books as there are.

For the book the naturalist would like to read may seem to him to be inaccessible: it is rare, or at any rate old and out of print, or it is too expensive for the ordinary individual, working by himself, to buy. The position of the serious student in such circumstances is to-day incomparably easier than it was thirty or forty years ago. There used to be at one time no alternative to making an application for a reader's ticket at the British Museum and, perhaps, travelling to London in order to make use of it in Bloomsbury; but now there is no need for this. The organisation of the Public Libraries has developed extraordinarily in the present generation, and, although the recent Centenary celebrations have done much to make known its various activities and the various services it offers, there are still three-quarters of the population who never use a Public Library at all. The naturalist will therefore be well advised to pay a visit to his nearest Public Library, for it is by no means improbable that the book he wants can be seen on its shelves. It is surprising what unexpected treasures the Reference Department of any Public Library may be found to contain. But even if the book is not there, there exists a system by which the Librarian can apply for it on a borrower's behalf and from some regional, central or specialised source of supply will obtain it for him.

This is done by every Librarian so many times every day that no one familiar with Public Libraries thinks very much about it; but if one pauses for a moment to consider, it can be seen to be a really remarkable event. When it is realised that little Miss Dash, living in a small town in Devonshire, is able, if she wishes, in a few days to consult the almost priceless pages of some seventeenth-century work on hand-made lace, the fact can be seen to be one of the undeniable benefits of modern civilisation.

But, to go a stage further than this, it may well be found that the naturalist has chosen for himself a group of animals about which no book exists. For instance, there is at present no book which deals wholly and authoritatively with British harvestmen or false-scorpions or ticks or any one of a dozen more groups, large or small. Information about these animals can be obtained only from scientific periodicals, the Journals, the Transactions or the Proceedings of learned bodies such as the Royal, the Linnean or the Zoological Societies. And it is very probable that most of the important papers which the naturalist wishes to read have been published in French or German journals.

There is usually no more difficulty in obtaining the required volumes of such a journal than in borrowing any other book, and it is here that the naturalist will show the toughness of his intellectual fibre and the genuineness of his enthusiasm. It is here too that he sees a real justification for the teaching of French and German in Public and Secondary schools. Modern languages as taught at school seldom become vehicles for much educational culture, and even less frequently is an ability to speak a language acquired in the classroom. But the advantage of being able to read the works of the greatest zoologists in Europe is one that cannot be exaggerated. In biological research this is often a necessity.

Do not be tempted to neglect this preliminary study of the

existing literature of your group by any suggestion that natural history is essentially an open-air occupation and that your own observations are the only part of it that need concern you, or by any advice that the only way to learn the biology of an animal is by practical work done by yourself. Of course your own observations, dissections and experiments are of the first importance to yourself, but this importance is no reason, as it is sometimes taken to be, for neglecting the work of others. One of the chief features of modern knowledge is the fact that ever since the printing of books became customary each generation is given the chance of starting where its predecessor left off. If you do not take this chance you limit yourself to mere amusement and waste of time, which may of course be all that some desire; but it is not what this book tries to suggest that you should do.

There is at least one popular natural history book known to me in which the writer describes on the first page a long-standing intention of adopting a little-known group of animals and studying it intensively, practically and independently, and then summarising all that had been learnt. At first sight the idea seems to have much to recommend it—the efforts of a pioneer, with a story of progress made, of set-backs, of difficulties overcome and of discoveries; and all this ought, it seems, to produce a valuable record of an individual's biological experience. Yet in practice it does not do so, because so much time and effort is spent in traversing the elementary stages and in exploring byways which should have been recognised as blind alleys.

To a beginner, access to the pages of the journals of learned societies may seem to be rather a formidable duty, though not a difficulty that cannot, perhaps, be overcome. It is certainly more important to know what these journals have published, and when.

It is all to the good of zoology that natural historians should be introduced, even early in their careers, to the *Zoological Record*. This mine of information has appeared annually since 1865—except during "World Wars" and the chaotic years which follow them, when there is an inevitable delay in production. It contains a virtually complete list of all books and papers that appeared in any language during the preceding year: it is conveniently divided into sections for different phyla or classes or animals and the sections can be bought separately. It follows that anyone who can consult a set of the annual volumes can readily compile

for himself a bibliography of all the published works that he
would like to read; he will also learn the names and nationalities
of those who are actively engaged in working at his group—information which is not always easily obtained otherwise. The following are the sections, with their prices as listed for 1953 :

	s.	d.			s.	d.
Comprehensive Zoology	2	6	Trilobita . . .	3	0
Protozoa . . .	7	6	Arachnida . . .	7	6
Porifera . . .	2	0	Insecta	30	0
Coelenterata . . .	4	0	Protochordata . .	2	0
Echinoderma . .	2	6	Pisces	7	0
Vermes . . .	10	0	Amphibia and Reptilia .	7	6
Brachiopoda . . .	3	0	Aves	7	6
Bryozoa . . .	2	0	Mammalia . . .	7	6
Mollusca . .	10	0	New Genera and sub-		
Crustacea . . .	5	0	genera . . .	3	0

It is clear that a naturalist who subscribes to the appropriate
section of the *Zoological Record* can keep himself up to date with
the progress that is being made in the study of the animals that
interest him most. This is an inestimable advantage—in fact the
Zoological Record deserves the widest possible support; for many
zoologists it is quite indispensable, and the annual arrival of the
blue-covered booklet which constitutes the section of one's choice
is invariably an encouragement and an inspiration.

Another feature of scientific journals, which is surprisingly unfamiliar to many natural historians, is their custom of supplying
their authors with reprinted copies of their papers. The writer of
a magazine story receives payment for his work; the writer of a
scientific article does not, but he is usually given 25 or possibly 50
copies of what he has written and is probably allowed to purchase
more at cost price. These he normally distributes to his friends
and to other zoologists who will, he believes, be interested in
them; and perhaps he has a surplus which he keeps in readiness
for those who may write and ask for them later.

It will be noticed that the cost of this falls on the author himself, but it may reasonably be pointed out that it is not as expensive a hobby as, shall we say, golf or photography, and that it
is usually of greater benefit to the zoologist. For it is in this way
that all those working at a subject interchange the results of their
labours and all are kept informed of progress in a much more

efficient way than could be achieved by merely hoping that all zoologists read all the journals—a task that no man could achieve.

The custom is international; there are tirés-à-part in France and separatischen Abdrücken in Germany, and so on, and their constant circulation shows a combination of generosity and co-operation which is not often conspicuous in human affairs.

It occasionally happens that collections of these reprints find their way into the second-hand bookshops, and the naturalist who comes upon them there has an opportunity which he should not miss of making a start in acquiring his own set of these invaluable objects. Then comes the time when he has written and published a paper of his own, when he can distribute his own reprints as wisely as possible.

He will find that he has sown seeds that will yield a rich harvest in the shape of a steadily growing library and an equally rapidly growing mailing-list of those with whom he is thus in constant touch. Often there grows from this interchange of writings a correspondence that overlaps the edges of the strictly scientific and becomes one of the many pleasurable by-products of a zoologist's life. From these generalisations I pass to more precise suggestions.

There are two series of books to which a naturalist should turn to see if his speciality has come within their survey. The first of these is undoubtedly the famous "New Naturalist" series which has been described without exaggeration as one of the major publishing ventures of the present century. Its handsome green volumes with their wealth of coloured and half-tone plates are sure to be familiar to all readers. Their principle is to emphasise the ecological treatment—to bring back into favour the old-fashioned natural history with the more precise foundation which modern science demands, and perhaps inevitably they tend at present towards the vertebrate, the conspicuous, the popular. But the appearance of that remarkable book *Fleas, Flukes and Cuckoos* shows that there is the possibility of a broadening horizon.

The second is the long series of annual publications of the Ray Society, instituted in 1843. These books are monographs which could not hope for publication in an ordinary commercial way, and which are quite invaluable to the specialist. The older volumes have of course been to a large extent superseded by advancing knowledge, and many of them are rare and almost unobtainable; but in the last thirty years volumes have been devoted to sea-anemones, spiders, water-beetles, to mention only a few.

A reference to Messrs. Frederick Warne & Co.'s famous "Wayside and Woodland Series" should hardly be necessary, for there can be but few naturalists of any age who have not quickly come to acknowledge their debt to these books. The success of their earlier volumes on such familiar subjects as wild flowers and butterflies has led to the inclusion of others less well-known, such as hymenopterous insects and two-winged flies. The books in this series are written by recognised specialists and are very well illustrated: their influence on the enthusiasm of many generations of naturalists must have been very great.

Reference should also be made to the extremely valuable but slow-growing series of "Synopses of the British Fauna," produced by the Linnean Society. At present there are only nine of these, but because of their low cost and their authoritative nature they deserve to be known as widely as possible. The nine deal with:

1. Harvestmen
2. Caprellidea
3. Gammaridae
4. Freshwater Bivalves
5. Freshwater Bivalves
6. Earthworms
7. Talitridae
8. Slugs
9. Woodlice

Finally, a selection of helpful works on small animals:

GENERAL

The Cambridge Natural History, 1895–19—. Macmillan.

The Standard Natural History, 1931. Warne.

M. Burr, *The Insect Legion*. (New Ed. 1954.) Nisbet.

G. H. Carpenter, *The Biology of Insects*, 1928. Sidgwick.

E. L. Daglish, *Name This Insect*, 1950. Dent.

A. E. Shipley, *Minor Horrors of War*, 1915. Cambridge.

E. Sandars, *An Insect Book for the Pocket*, 1946. Oxford.

EARTHWORMS

F. E. Beddard, *A Monograph of the Order of Oligochaeta*, 1895. Oxford.

A. C. Evans, "Earthworms and the Soil," *Discovery*, ix, 1948.

J. Stephenson, *The Oligochaeta*, 1930. Oxford.

WOODLICE

W. M. Webb and C. Sillem, *British Woodlice*, 1906. Duckworth.

W. E. Collinge, *A Revised Checklist of the British Terrestrial Isopoda*, 1918. British Museum.

E. B. Edney, "The Woodlice of Great Britain and Ireland," *Proc. Linn. Soc.*, clxiv, 1953.

EARWIGS AND COCKROACHES

M. Burr, *British Grasshoppers and their Allies*, 1936. Alan.
W. J. Lucas, *British Orthoptera*, 1920. Dulan.

ANTS

H. St. J. K. Donisthorpe, *British Ants*, 1927. Routledge.
H. St. J. K. Donisthorpe, *Guests of British Ants*. Routledge.
D. W. Morley, *The Ant World*, 1953. Penguin Books.
E. Step, *Bees, Wasps, Ants and Allied Insects of the British Isles*, 1932. Warne.

DRAGONFLIES

C. Longfield, *Dragonflies of the British Isles*, 1937. Warne.
W. J. Lucas, *British Dragonflies*, 1899. Gill.

MOSQUITOES

F. W. Edwards, *British Mosquitoes and their Control*, 1934.
F. W. Edwards, *Mosquitoes and their Relation to Disease*, 1931.
(The two volumes are published by the British Museum.)
J. F. Marshall, *British Mosquitoes*, 1938. Oxford.

CENTIPEDES AND MILLIPEDES

S. G. Brade-Birks, "Notes on Myriapoda," *J. S.-E. Afric. Coll.*, Wye, 1934 and 1939.
J. Cloudsley-Thompson, "Biology of Centipedes and Millipedes," *Discovery*, xiii, 1952.
E. H. Eason, "Notes on Chilopoda," *Ann. Mag. Nat. Hist.*, iv, 1951, 257.

HARVESTMEN AND FALSE-SCORPIONS

O. Pickard-Cambridge, *Monograph of the British Phalangidea*, 1890. Sime, Dorchester.
O. Pickard-Cambridge, *On the British Species of Chernetidae*, 1892. Sime, Dorchester.
T. H. Savory, *Spiders and Allied Orders of the British Isles*, 1945. Warne.

SLUGS

A. E. Ellis, *British Snails*, 1926. Oxford.
H. F. Barnes, "The Slugs in our Gardens," *New Biology*, No. 6. Penguin Books.

PART TWO

NOTE

THE twelve chapters which follow are intended to be read as short introductions to the study of twelve typical groups of "small animals"; they are not intended to be more than introductions which will enable readers to decide whether or not any particular group interests them.

If it does, then the earliest steps towards specialisation are here, I hope, simplified; but no chapter is intended to be either a miniature monograph or a fully documented and illustrated account of any section of the British fauna. Illustrations, in particular, have been kept to a minimum, and all the really important and valuable work to be done by a specialist has been left to the enthusiast to do for himself.

Chapter XI

EARTHWORMS

FOR a very long time Earthworms have attracted the attention of those interested in the cultivation of crops. Nearly two hundred years ago Gilbert White, author of the well-known *Natural History of Selborne*, stated that "the soil soon becomes cold, hard bound, and void of fermentation and consequently sterile" if Earthworms were not plentiful and active in it. In 1881 Charles Darwin published his famous book *The Formation of Vegetable Mould Through the Action of Worms*, and in it he wrote, "It may be doubted whether there are any other animals which have played such an important part in the history of the world as these lowly organised creatures." Emphatic words like these, from so eminent a scientist, ought to have ensured a general biological interest in the animals which inspired them, yet when Dr. A. C. Evans first undertook research into the biology of Earthworms at Rothamsted in 1945 he found that there was no existing knowledge of even the outlines of the life-history of a single species. There could scarcely be a better example of the neglect of common creatures which has already been mentioned.

General Appearance. The appearance of an Earthworm is both simple and familiar, but attention must be drawn to features which are inconspicuous, and to others that are useful in classifying and distinguishing species.

The obvious characteristic of the Earthworm's tubular body is its segmentation. It is made of a number of clearly visible rings or segments, and in the hinder part of the body these are all very much alike. The front end, which is more rounded than flattened, shows a little more elaboration.

The first segment, often loosely called the head, contains the mouth and bears an almost spherical projection, the prostomium. The shape of this organ, which is a very sensitive part, well supplied with nerves, differs

A · PROLOBOUS
B · EPILOBOUS-ALLOLOBOPHORA
C · TANYLOBOUS-LUMBRICUS

FIG. 5.—Types of Prostomium

78

in different genera, and one of the first things to look at when identifying an Earthworm is the way in which the prostomium is fitted into the rest of the segment, or peristomium. The different types and their names are shown in Figure 5.

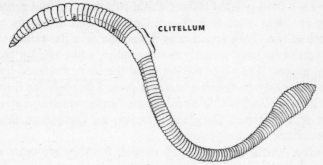

CLITELLUM

FIG. 6.—An Earthworm (× ⅔)

The girdle, properly called the clitellum, is the next feature to attract attention. This is a region, covering four to eight segments, where the skin is thickened and glandular and differs in colour from the rest of the animal. It is often mistaken as evidence of the popular belief that the worm has been cut in two and the two halves have joined together again. Needless to say it is nothing of the kind; it is a glandular region which secretes the cocoon in which the Earthworm lays its eggs. It is also a sign that the worm is full-grown, an important point, for beginners will be well advised not to attempt to determine the name of an immature specimen.

Earthworms are hermaphroditic, that is to say each individual possesses both male and female organs, and both systems open on the lower side of the anterior part of the body. The male orifices are usually the easiest to see, since they are guarded by large lip-like edges; in the commonest species these are on segment 15. The openings of the oviducts, which are just in front of them, are much less conspicuous.

The body of the Earthworm is covered from end to end by a smooth glistening cuticle, which facilitates the gliding of the animal between the particles of soil and at the same time protects the softer muscular tissue. It is lubricated by glands in the skin and is therefore perforated where glands or other organs open to the exterior. If a dead worm is left to soak in water for some time the whole of the cuticle can be drawn off as a structureless iridescent envelope.

With a few exceptions each segment of an Earthworm's body bears a number of setae (also written in the Greek form chaetae). These are hard pointed rods of chitin (see page 19) and generally there are eight setae to each segment, arranged uniformly or in groups of two. They function as limbs, enabling the animal to fix one part of its body securely in the ground, while another part is being moved. The slight roughness of the body produced by the setae can easily be felt if a worm is passed through the fingers: they make a clearly audible noise as an Earthworm creeps across a sheet of newspaper. On glass, however, an Earthworm finds it more difficult to make progress.

Habits. Earthworms are well named, for they are more continuously earthbound than most other animals. Other creatures dig burrows for the protection of themselves and their young, but the Earthworm lives in the soil and travels through it almost as other animals live in air or water.

The way in which they move has already been partly outlined. With the setae of the middle and hinder segments thrust into the soil, the forepart of the body is driven forwards by strong muscular action. To anyone who has handled a worm, and found it to be soft and by no means rigid, this sounds impossible. That it is not so is due to the fact that the body is filled with a liquid, the coelomic fluid; muscle fibres placed circularly round the body contract, reduce the worm's diameter and, pressing on this fluid, make the fore-end rigid enough to slide forwards. The anterior setae now grip the sides of the burrow, the circular muscles relax and a layer of longitudinal muscles contracts. This shortens the body, the middle portion of which, its setae withdrawn, now follows the front. Lastly a repetition of the process brings up the tail. Thus waves of contraction with extension and expansion with shortening seem to pass continuously along the Earthworm's body.

At the same time, movement is assisted by a sucking action produced by the pharynx just behind the animal's gullet. This draws some of the soil into the worm's body and it is from the digestible constituents of these swallowed mouthfuls of earth that the Earthworm obtains much of its food. The earth passes from the crop to a muscular gizzard, containing pieces of grit which, like the stones

A Cockroach.

Red ants.
A queen, worker and
eggs.

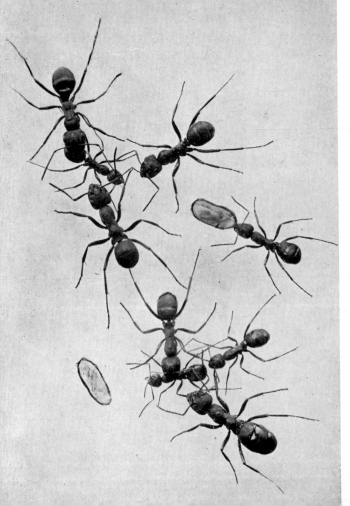

Red ants on a slave
raid. The oval objects
are the cocoons of the
attacked species, one
of which is being
carried off.

in a bird's gizzard, grind up the contents. The finely-divided soil then passes through the intestine. The wormcasts which are familiar to everyone are produced in this way, but only by two species of the genus Allolobophora; other Earthworms deposit the residues underground.

Earthworms are essentially nocturnal animals. A proportion of their activities even at night are limited to coming to the tops of their burrows and with their tails still anchored therein exploring the ground in a circle with their fore-parts. In this way they may meet at the proper season another Earthworm with which to mate, and they may find leaves, which they seize and drag partly underground.

They may easily be kept in jam-pots of moist earth. The glass sides of the jam-pots should usually be covered with a movable cylinder of dark paper, when a proportion of the burrows will travel along the inside of the glass and the movements of the animals within can be watched by temporarily removing the paper. If this is not done they will avoid the light and be invisible in the centre.

This shows that the Earthworm, though it has no eyes, is sensitive to light, and it appears that light falling on almost any part of its body is able to provoke a response. It is also well known that Earthworms respond to vibrations in a way that corresponds to the hearing of higher animals. Stamping the foot on the ground will cause them to retreat into their burrows, but other disturbances, such as hammering or moving a stick thrust into the soil, will often make them emerge. It follows that they must possess some sense organ that distinguishes between "up" and "down." They must further possess the power of responding to such stimuli as smell and taste, for they quickly move towards certain edible objects, such as raw meat and onions, when these are brought into their neighbourhood. In their habit of drawing leaves into their burrows and gradually consuming the tips, they show an obvious selective power, for if a variety of leaves are offered them some will always be chosen before others. There is scope for much investigation of this habit.

Life-History. Earthworms are hermaphroditic but not self-fertilising. Two animals lying close to each other become temporarily united by a band of slimy mucus secreted by cells in the skin. Each receives spermatozoa from the other, and stores them in special sacs called spermathecae. The eggs are laid in a cocoon. This is produced as a cylinder by the cells of the girdle or clitellum and the animal wriggles out of it backwards. As it passes the openings of the oviducts the eggs are shed into it, and the spermatozoa follow when the spermathecae are reached. Fertilisation thus occurs in the cocoon, the ends of which close up as the earthworm finally withdraws its head.

A cocoon, an oval horny brown capsule, contains from one to a score of eggs, according to species. Sometimes the worms that hatch first eat the eggs that have not done so. The young remain in the cocoon for several weeks, and become mature about a year after they have left it. In nature the length of their lives is of course fortuitous, but in captivity Lumbricus terrestris has lived for six years and Allolobophora for ten.

Systematics. British Earthworms belong to the large family of over two hundred species known as the Lumbricidae, in the order Oligochaeta. In most European countries the Earthworm fauna is divisible into two parts, the native species which are now found in rather restricted areas and which are known as the endemic species, and the immigrants, called the peregrine species, which are widely dispersed over most of the continent. In Britain there are 17 common peregrine species, and 8 endemic.

List of British Earthworms

FAMILY LUMBRICIDAE

Lumbricus castaneus (Savigny)
Lumbricus festivus (Savigny)
Lumbricus friendi (Cognetti)
Lumbricus rubellus Hoffmeister
Lumbricus terrestris Linnaeus
Allolobophora caliginosa (Savigny)
Allolobophora chlorotica (Savigny)
Allolobophora icteria (Savigny)
Allolobophora nocturna Evans
Allolobophora terrestris (Savigny)
Bimastus beddardi (Michaelsen)
Bimastus eiseni (Levinsen)
Bimastus icenorum Pickford
Bimastus tenuis (Eisen)
Dendrobaena mammalis (Savigny)

Dendrobaena octaedra (Savigny)
Dendrobaena subrubicunda (Eisen)
Dendrobaena rubida (Savigny)
Eisenia foetida (Savigny)
Eisenia rosea (Savigny)
Eisenia veneta Rosa
Eiseniella tetraedra (Savigny)
Eophila oculata (Hoffmeister)
Octolasium cyaneum (Savigny)
Octolasium lacteum Oerley

The largest British Earthworm, which is also one of the commonest, to be found in almost every garden, is Lumbricus terrestris. It may reach a length of 30 cm. Quite as common is L. rubellus, the "red worm" of the angler, which is rather more than half this size. The "marsh worm," about 3 cm. long, with an orange clitellum, is L. castaneus, found everywhere in Britain.

The Earthworm which is most frequently mistaken for L. terrestris is either Allolobophora caliginosa or A. terrestris. Both species, which are epilobic, are common and widespread and in colour are a murky grey-brown, contrasting with the clear red-violet of Lumbricus. A. caliginosa, reaching 7 cm., is smaller than A. terrestris, which may be 12 cm. long. A. chlorotica, varying between green, yellow, grey and blue, is also widely distributed.

In the genus Bimastus the commonest British species is B. tenuis, a reddish-brown worm up to 8 cm. long, lighter coloured underneath; it is usually found in moss and leaf-mould or under rotting wood in moist situations.

The genus Dendrobaena includes two species known to fishermen as the Cockspur or Gilt-tail; these are D. subrubicunda, one of our commonest species, and D. rubida. Both have the last few segments coloured yellow. The former which, reaching 9 cm., is the larger, has a rosy rather flattened body; the latter is more cylindrical and is darker above than below.

The Brandling, another anglers' favourite, is Eisenia foetida, usually an inhabitant of manure heaps. It is red, brown or purple, with orange bands, and when irritated emits a turbid yellow fluid with a pungent smell. The Mucous worm, E. rosea, is a very common species, easily recognisable by its large clitellum, the segments of which are almost twice as broad as those of the rest of the body.

The genus Eiseniella contains but one British species, E. tetrae-dra, a small amphibious worm about 3 cm. long and remarkable in being quadrangular behind the clitellum. It is common in the banks of streams all over this country and usually lives immersed in water.

The two species of the genus Octolasium are fairly common. O. cyaneum is a slatey-blue worm, often with a violet dorsal line, a red clitellum and a yellow tail, exuding a turbid fluid. It may reach a length of 18 cm. O. lacteum, which is the more frequent, is milky white or blue with an orange or pink clitellum.

This short survey of the commonest species of British Earth-worms is based on the typical forms, but, like slugs, Earthworms are very variable creatures, and therefore not only difficult but often impossible to identify with certainty from an external examination alone. Even the separation of the family into genera demands a comparison of internal organs, visible only on dissec-tion; in consequence a simple key for identification, such as is given for most of the other groups in this book, cannot be con-structed.

Chapter XII

WOODLICE

WOODLICE are to be included among those interesting animals which have broken away from the habits and traditions of their relatives and have so thoroughly adapted themselves to new circumstances that no evidence of their ancestry is revealed to a casual glance. An examination of a Woodlouse shows that it is a Crustacean, yet one that is so completely terrestrial that its relationship to a shrimp or a barnacle seems to be very obscure.

General Appearance. All Woodlice have an oval-shaped body, arched above and very clearly segmented. It consists of a head, a thorax of seven segments and an abdomen of six segments. The segments of the abdomen are usually narrower than those of the thorax and are easily distinguishable.

The head bears two small eyes, which are never raised above the surface as are the "stalk-eyes" of such Crustacea as lobsters. They may be either simple eyes, ocelli, with a smooth surface, or compound, like the larger eyes of insects. There are two pairs of antennae, a typically crustacean characteristic. The first pair, of only three segments, are very small and can be seen only from below, where they are situated between the bases of the second pair.

The second pair of antennae are the conspicuous sensory organs, which a living Woodlouse can be seen to be actively using. Each second antenna is composed of several segments, the exact number of which varies in the different genera and species, and which, with their relative

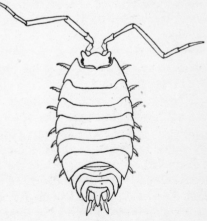

Fig. 7.—A Woodlouse (× 4)

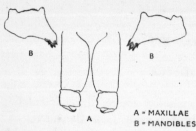

A = MAXILLAE
B = MANDIBLES

Fig. 8.—Mouth-parts of Oniscus (× 10)

lengths, is often a most important guide to the determination of species. These antennae are customarily carried in a characteristic bent position, as if there were an elbow-joint in the middle. The terminal segment beyond the elbow are called the flagellum of the antenna, and are generally a specific feature of each kind of Woodlouse.

Woodlice have comparatively elaborate mouth-parts, which are examined from the lower surface, and which for study can be separated from the head of a Woodlouse gently boiled in dilute caustic potash. There are four pairs, the mandibles, the first maxillae, the second maxillae and the maxillipeds. When these parts are being investigated the maxillipeds are the first to be seen, as large ovoid organs, covering the others. These parts are all paired structures, furnished at their extremities with hard teeth or stiff setae to break up the food and carry it to the mouth. The mouth is a small opening, between the mandibles, with two appendages usually described as the "upper lip" and the "lower lip."

Each of the seven segments of the thorax carries a pair of legs. These are quite typical crustacean legs, like those of a crayfish, and are constructed of seven hard tubular parts, terminating in a claw. In the female Woodlouse the second to the fifth thoracic segments also carry each a pair of plate-like processes, which overlap in the middle and so produce a space under the ventral plates of the thorax. This is the brood-pouch, in which the eggs are carried.

The six segments of the abdomen also carry appendages. These are not leg-like but plate-like in form (except the last pair), and consist of an inner and an outer portion. The inner plate is a gill, by which the blood of the Woodlouse is aerated as long as it is surrounded by moist air, while the outer plate is a harder, protective cover. This dependence on atmospheric moisture shows that the Woodlouse's adaptation to a land life is not as complete as it may appear to be, but in some species a further stage is to be seen. In Porcellio, for instance, the outer plates of the first two pairs of abdominal appendages are marked with white spots, which are really tufts of fine branching tubes, penetrating the appendage. These tubes or tracheae are full of air and open to the exterior by a small pore. Thus they enable the animal to make use of atmospheric oxygen and may represent the beginnings of a tracheal system such as has developed independently in the insects.

The first and second abdominal appendages of a male Woodlouse are modified from the typical form. The inner "plates" are no longer flat but are long pointed rods.

The sixth pair of abdominal appendages form the uropods. They are the pointed structures that can usually be seen at the hinder end of a Woodlouse and between them the abdomen terminates in a pointed telson. The uropods of the male are usually larger than those of the female.

Life-History. The formation of a special brood-pouch under the thorax of the female Woodlouse is mentioned above. The oviducts open on the fifth thoracic segment, just inside the base of each fifth leg, so that the eggs are laid directly into the brood-pouch, and develop there. In most of the common species the eggs are laid at the beginning of the summer and hatch about five weeks later.

There is no larval form, but the tiny Woodlice, which are retained for a time in the pouch, have only six pairs of legs, the seventh pair being rudimentary. After the first moult the seventh pair appear in their normal form and the Woodlouse slowly grows to its adult size.

General Habits. Woodlice are restricted in their wanderings by the necessity for moist gills, with the result that they are found in places where moisture is prevalent and therefore nearly always underneath some solid object which protects them from the sun. Stones and logs of wood, the bark of dead trees and all such things are likely to harbour Woodlice, which may be found by looking beneath them, often in considerable numbers. Decaying vegetable matter and heaps of stable manure are also favourite haunts, and Woodlice may also be found in long grass and in moss in damp places.

Their food is mixed. They eat at night or in the early morning, and may choose seedling plants or stored vegetables, thus making

themselves unpopular with the gardener. But animal matter and
refuse of all kinds may be consumed, and they occasionally eat
each other.

This cannibalism usually occurs after the victim has moulted,
and the casting of a Woodlouse's skin is a very peculiar process.
Before the moult takes place, the edges of the segments turn white
as the old cuticle separates from the new one beneath. The Woodlouse seeks a hiding-place or excavates a small burrow; its skin
then breaks between the fourth and fifth thoracic segments. The
animal, walking forwards out of the hinder portion of its old coat,
pulls the legs of the fifth, sixth and seventh segments from their
tubular covers. The moulted skin is eaten, and for about three
days the creature has a very remarkable appearance, with the
white edges still to be seen on the front segments and the posterior
part pale, soft and slightly disproportionate because it is a little
larger.

When the tail is hard the skin of the head and the anterior
thoracic segments is pushed off. It is now that the Woodlouse's
care in concealment is justified, for its mouth-parts are too soft for
it to be able either to feed or to defend itself, and it is a ready
victim to any predator. In a few days, however, these parts have
hardened and the animal eats the second half of its old skin as its
first meal in its new condition.

One of the most remarkable phenomena in the biology of
Woodlice is the existence of monogeny, or the production of a
brood all the members of which are of the same sex, or in which
one sex is much more numerous than the other. This is found in
Armadillidium vulgare, Trichoniscus pusillus and Ligidium
hypnorum, and the reason for it is at present imperfectly known.

The commonest Woodlice in Britain are Oniscus asellus and
Porcellio scaber, which occur almost everywhere and usually in
large numbers. Clearly they are less rigidly confined to special
types of micro-climates than the others. Platyarthrus is the blind
white Woodlouse familiar to all who look into ants' nests, where
it is a permanent guest. Cylisticus and all the Armadillidiidae can
roll themselves into a sphere. To the mediaeval surgeons this suggested the use of the "armadillo" or hog-louse as medicine for
the liver and digestive organs. The rolled-up Woodlouse was
administered alive, both to human beings and to cattle. These
Woodlice are often confused with the "pill-millipedes," which

also roll themselves up, but the latter when unrolled can be seen to have far more than seven pairs of legs.

Systematics. Woodlice, as has been said, are Crustacea which have become adapted to terrestrial life, and within this class they form the order Isopoda. There are thirty-seven British species, which are contained in five families.

List of British Woodlice

ORDER ISOPODA

Family Ligiidae
    Ligia oceanica (L.)
    Ligidium hypnorum (Cuvier)
Family Trichoniscidae
    Trichoniscoides albidus (B-Lund)
    Trichoniscoides sarsi Patience
    Trichoniscus pusillus Brandt
    Trichoniscus pygmaeus Sars
    Cordioniscus stebbingi (Patience)
    Cordioniscus spinosus (Patience)
    Androniscus dentiger Verhoeff
    Androniscus weberi Verhoeff
    Miktoniscus linearis (Patience)
    Oritoniscus flavus (B-Lund)
    Haplophthalmus mengii (Zaddach)
    Haplophthalmus danicus B-Lund
Family Oniscidae
    Philoscia muscorum (Scopoli)
    Halophiloscia couchii (Kinahan)
    Chaetophiloscia patiencei (Bagnall)
    Platyarthrus hoffmannseggi Brandt
    Oniscus asellus L.
Family Porcellionidae
    Cylisticus convexus (Degeer)
    Metoponorthus pruinosus (Brandt)
    Metoponorthus cingendus (Kinahan)
    Metoponorthus melanurus B-Lund
    Porcellio scaber Latreille
    Porcellio laevis Latreille
    Porcellio spinicornis Say
    Porcellio dilatatus Brandt

Porcellio rathkei (Brandt)
Porcellio ratzeburgi (Brandt)
Family Armadillidiidae
Armadillidium opacum (Koch)
Armadillidium vulgare (Latreille)
Armadillidium pulchellum (Zencker)
Armadillidium pictum Brandt
Armadillidium album Dollfus
Armadillidium depressum Brandt
Armadillidium nasatum B-Lund
Eluma purpurascens B-Lund

The following is a shortened form of a key which should help beginners to name the commoner British Woodlice. Several of the rare or very local species have been omitted. It should be remembered that in some species the colour varies very considerably; also it should be pointed out that the experts in this branch of natural history rely to a large extent on exact measurements of length to breadth ratio in the rami of the uropods. The serious student is advised to consult the account given by E. B. Edney in the *Proceedings of the Linnean Society*, Vol. 164, 1953, pp. 49–98.

1(2)	Flagellum of antennae with 10 or more segments	3
2(1)	Flagellum of antennae with fewer than 10 segments	5
3(4)	Littoral; large, up to 3 cm. long	Ligia oceanica
4(3)	Terrestrial; smaller, up to 1 cm.	Ligidium hypnorum
5(6)	Rami of uropods similar	7
6(5)	Rami dissimilar, exopodite much broader than endopodite	21
7(10)	Outline of body smoothly continuous	8
8(9)	Tergites with longitudinal ridges	Haplophthalmus mengii
9(8)	Tergites with rows of tubercles	Haplophthalmus danicus
10(7)	Abdomen narrower than thorax	11
11(16)	Each eye a single ocellus	12
12(13)	Rose-pink; up to 5.5 mm. long	Androniscus dentiger
13(12)	About 4 mm. long	14
14(15)	Flagellum of four segments	Trichoniscoides albidus
15(14)	Flagellum of three segments	Trichoniscoides sarsi
16(11)	Eyes with three ocelli	17
17(18)	Flagellum of three segments; 2.5 mm.; whitish	Trichoniscus pygmaeus
18(17)	Flagellum of four segments	19
19(20)	Reddish, mottled; 4 mm.	Trichoniscus pusillus

20(19) Dark red-brown; 3 mm.   Cordioniscus stebbingi

21(46) Endopodites of uropods visible from above   22

22(29) No pseudotracheae   23

23(26) Abdomen narrower than thorax   24

24(25) Telson pointed posteriorly   Philoscia muscorum

25(24) Telson rounded; littoral   Halophiloscia couchii

26(23) Outline of body smoothly continuous   27

27(28) No eyes; myrmecophilous; white   Platyarthrus hoffmannseggi

28(27) Eyes present   Oniscus asellus *

29(22) Pseudotracheae present   30

30(31) Able to roll into a ball   Cylisticus convexus

31(30) Unable to roll   32

32(35) Abdomen narrower than thorax   33

33(34) Tergites of thorax with transverse keel

                    Metoponorthus cingendus

34(33) Tergites of thorax smooth   Metoponorthus pruinosus

35(32) Outline of body smoothly continuous   36

36(39) Over 15 mm.   37

37(38) Ubiquitous; usually dark grey   Porcellio scaber *

38(37) Light grey; very long antennae   Porcellio laevis

39(36) Not more than 15 mm.   40

40(41) 10 mm.; grey   Porcellio ratzeburgi

41(40) 12–15 mm.   42

42(43) Dark brown   Porcellio spinicornis

43(42) Not dark brown   **44**

44(45) Light grey   Porcellio dilatatus

45(44) Greyish-brown   Porcellio rathkei

46(21) Endopodites of uropods invisible from above   47

47(50) Large; more than 17 mm.   48

48(49) Ubiquitous; black   Armadillidium vulgare

49(48) Slatey-grey   Armadillidium depressum

50(47) Less than 11 mm.   51

51(52) Less than 4 mm.; dark brown with 5 irregular pale spots

                 Armadillidium pulchellum

52(51) More than 4 mm.; greyish-brown   53

53(54) 7 mm.; 3 rows of light spots   Armadillidium pictum

54(53) 10 mm.; longitudinal rows of dark marks

                 Armadillidium nasatum

Chapter XIII

SILVER-FISH

IF towards evening in spring or summer we go into the scullery or larder of almost any of the older houses of this country and there look among the bottles on the shelves, if we move the packets of food or lift the sack of potatoes, we shall be nearly certain to disturb a shining grey insect, with a narrow tapering body and short legs, which obviously deserves its popular name of Silver-fish. We must be quick to catch it, for it can run as quickly as the cockroaches, with which it is perhaps sharing the room, but when caught it is well worth our attention as an example of an insect that has no wings.

General Appearance. The whole body of a Silver-fish is covered with characteristic scales, which are probably a modified form of the "hairs" found on the bodies of most other insects. The scales are easily rubbed off; they are smooth and lustrous and give the animal its burnished metallic appearance.

The head bears a pair of long jointed antennae above and a pair of mandibles or jaws below. These mandibles, which are merely able to bite or crush the food-particles, are very like the mandibles of a cockroach and are of a kind usually found in insects of a primitive type. There are two eyes.

The thorax is quite typical of insects in consisting of three segments, each carrying a pair of short legs.

There are ten segments to the abdomen, all clearly visible and distinct from one another. The tenth bears three long jointed processes or cerci, remarkably similar to the antennae, and to which is due the common name of Bristle-tails for the order to which the Silver-fish belongs.

In all ordinary familiar insects the legs belong to the thorax only and the abdomen has no limbs or appendages on its under side. But this is not true of the Bristle-tails, where some of the segments possess small rod-like organs, placed at the sides of the hind edge of the ventral plates. They are provided with muscles, but their function is something of a mystery: it is possible that they help to support the long body and it has also been thought that they are organs of touch. An insect learns far more by touch than does a man; there are many small animals in whose daily lives the sense of touch is of greater importance and value than any other.

There are also several small vesicles, situated near these abdominal appendages, which can be extruded from the body or withdrawn into it. They provide another mystery: perhaps they have a respiratory use.

The eighth and ninth segments of the abdomen carry the reproductive organs or gonapophyses.

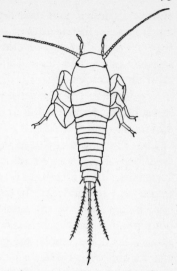

Fig. 9.—A Silver-fish (× 3)

Life-History. The Silver-fish lays from seven to twelve eggs, dropped almost anywhere and neither glued to the floor nor hidden or protected. Hence they will always have the same temperature as their surroundings, which will vary; and they appear to be influenced by the moisture of the air. In consequence the eggs will sometimes hatch six days after they have been laid; in different circumstances they may take ten times as long as this. The young ones resemble their parents except in size, and in having, at first, no scales; that is to say they are nymphs which have only to grow, not larvae which are going to change into pupae. They take a year and a half, or more, to become full-grown.

Habits. The usual food of the Silver-fish is floury, starchy or sugary matter such as is likely to be found in the domestic store-cupboard. It is more of a scavenger than a pest. It may also eat the paste off detached fragments of wall-paper, and has a reputation, very probably undeserved, for injuring papers by biting their edges, and damaging books by attacking the paste and glue of their bindings.

Although they can easily be banished from a room or a house by almost any of the common insecticides, it seems as a rule scarcely worth while to do so. They are interesting creatures, entirely harmless, and their depredations do not normally cost as much as the substances required to kill them. There is no obvious reason why Silver-fish should not be kept under observation in suitable cages, and their habits and behaviour more fully and carefully recorded.

Systematics. The primitive wingless insects are placed together in a sub-class known as the Apterygota, with three orders, Protura, Thysanura and Collembola.

The Thysanura includes the Silver-fish, Lepisma saccharina, described above, and its near relative the Fire-brat, Thermobia furnorum. The Fire-brat is slightly the larger; it is darker in colour and rather hairy. It lives only in warmer places, such as bake-houses, and in the immediate neighbourhood of ovens or hot pipes. On the beach Machilis maritimus is often found. It has some black scales among the grey, which give it a simple pattern, and its abdomen carries a pair of vestigial appendages on every segment except the first. Of the three abdominal cerci the middle one is distinctly the longest, whereas the three are almost the same length in Lepisma. The allied species Machilis polypoda occurs inland.

The Collembola or Spring-tails are often to be found, sometimes in large numbers, among drifted leaves in ditches and under hedges. When the leaves are disturbed they leap vigorously about, at once betraying their nature by this remarkable habit. They have but six * abdominal segments, to the fourth or fifth of which is attached the great "saltatorial appendage" or spring. When at rest this organ is held in a "catch" on the third segment, and when released it propels the animal upwards with rocket-like force. A number of species occur in Britain, the most often found being Orchesella cincta. This is a variable species, usually recognisable by the golden or orange band across its back. The famous Antarctic insects, Gomphiocephalus hodgsoni, almost the only permanent land fauna of the Antarctic continent, are also members of this order.

---

* This shows that they cannot be regarded as primitive insects; or perhaps, according to recent opinion, not insects at all.

Chapter XIV

EARWIGS

THERE are, perhaps, more puzzles associated with the Earwig than with any other insect that is as well-known and as widely distributed. Its name, for instance, is a mystery, for it has no relation or connexion with the human or any other ear and is not in the habit of entering ears, and yet not only the common English name, but also the French, perce-oreille, and the German, Ohrenwurm, have the same suggestion. Further, it has wings which are folded as elaborately as an airman's parachute and which seem to be as seldom used, as well as a pair of abdominal forceps, the function of which is doubtful.

General Appearance. Earwigs are rather primitive insects and, like most insects of this character, their mouth-parts are designed for biting.

The mandibles are hard, strong organs, each made in a single piece, curved on the outer edge and bearing on the inner two pointed teeth and a roughened grinding area. They move transversely towards each other and thus masticate anything that comes between them.

Behind each mandible is one of the first maxillae, consisting of a short basal piece, the cardo, a longer median one, the stipes, and two terminal lobes, the lacinia and galea. The stipes bears on its outer edge a maxillary palp, which functions as a tactile organ.

The second maxillae are fused together in the middle line and close the Earwig's mouth from behind. They consist of essentially the same parts as the first maxillae.

The head of the Earwig also

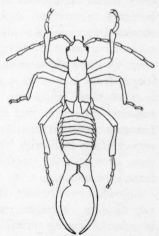

FIG. 10.—A Male Earwig (× 2)

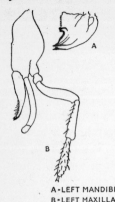

A·LEFT MANDIBLE
B·LEFT MAXILLA

Fig. 11.—Mouth-parts
of Forficula (× 10)

bears two pairs of long thread-like antennae of fourteen segments and a pair of large faceted eyes, but no simple ocelli.

The thorax is composed of three distinct and independent segments. Each segment carries a pair of legs and the legs of an Earwig are usually far apart. On the upper surface the second and third segments of the thorax carry the wing-covers and the wings. The former are hard, short and flat, and the wings, which lie folded beneath, project slightly from the hind margin. The wings when expanded have a curious shape, something like that of a human ear. They are extremely delicate and they are folded up in a remarkably complex way, which few other insects can show. It is probable that in the elaborate process of folding them up the forceps are of some assistance.

The abdomen is composed of ten segments, but in the common Earwig only eight of these can be seen in the female.

The characteristic forceps on the tenth segment are usually curved in the male and straight in the female. They are something of a puzzle for they are not known to be used in fighting and as weapons of defence the nip that they can give is rather feeble. The chief biological interest of these forceps lies in their marked tendency to variation, especially in the male of the commonest species. In a classical study of this matter, Bateson and Brindley collected a thousand earwigs on one day on the Farne Islands in 1892. Of these 583 were mature males and their forceps varied in length from 2 mm. to 9 mm. The distribution of individuals between these limits was, however, not uniform but showed a tendency to concentrate about lengths of 3·5 mm. and 7 mm. No such variation has been detected among the females. The variety of the male with long forceps, known as the macrolabious form, is by no means rare.

Life-History. The common Earwig displays a maternal care that is unusual among primitive insects. In the late autumn a pair

Fig. 12.—Leg of Forficula (× 10)

Carpenter ants "at home"
in a decayed log.

Ants (*Formica rufa*)
dragging the body of a
dead cockchafer beetle
back to their nest.

Dragonfly recently emerged from its pupa, the wings not yet expanded.

of Earwigs begin to hibernate together, continuing in close companionship for several months. The male leaves the nest in the early spring, when the eggs are laid, but the female remains, "sitting on" the eggs like a hen and guarding them with apparent devotion. It is said that they will not hatch unless they thus receive her attention, and it is certain that if she is disturbed and the eggs are scattered, she will collect them into a heap once more.

Young Earwigs, like young silver-fish and young cockroaches, are not larvae but nymphs. They have neither wings nor elytra at first. As soon as they are hatched they creep under the abdomen and between the legs of their mother, if she is still alive, and she continues for a while to watch over them. Whether the other species of British Earwigs behave in the same way appears to be unknown.

Habits. A little is known of the habits of the common Earwig and almost nothing about the habits of the others. Probably they are chiefly carnivorous animals, and the gardener's dislike of the Earwig is not easy to justify. They may, perhaps, nibble the delicate petals and leaves of flowers and vegetables, but much of the damage often attributed to them is likely to be due to other insects. They may be seen feeding at the wounds of such animals as rats that have been bitten by dogs and mice that have been killed by cats, and there is little doubt that their preference is for flesh food.

They generally become active in the evening and during most of the hours of daylight they lie concealed in crevices and in all kinds of dark, narrow hiding-places.

The wings of the common Earwig seem to be used but seldom. It is often assumed that these insects do not fly and that the individuals that have on occasion been seen on the wing were in some way abnormal. Perhaps they were only abnormal in flying at a time when they could be seen; but in any case there are a number of records of large numbers of flying Earwigs seen in a short time, so that it is unreasonable to describe them all as abnormal. Moreover, the stomachs of bats often contain Earwig remains. Flight, however, is certainly one of the items in an Earwig's habits which calls for further investigation. This concerns the common species only: the small species known as Labia minor is normally a flier.

Earwigs may be found nearly all the year round. Sweeping, especially in nettle-beds, and beating low shrubs are the best ways of collecting them. Also the provision of resting-places for the daytime, such as a bunch of straw, is an attention which they will often appreciate. They do not seem to be at all difficult to keep in captivity.

Systematics. Earwigs belong to an order known as the Dermaptera. They were formerly included with the cockroaches and grasshoppers in the Orthoptera. The Dermaptera number nearly nine hundred species, five of which are natives of Britain. Three immigrant species, however, are also well-established in this country but live only indoors, in artificial conditions, where the temperature is high. They are neither conspicuous nor numerous.

List of British Earwigs

NATIVE

Forficula auricularia L.
Forficula lesnei Finot
Labidura riparia (Pallas)
Labia minor (L.)
Apterygida albipennis (Megerle)

IMPORTED

Prolabia arachidis (Yersin)
Anisolabis maritima (Bonelli)
Anisolabis annulipes (Lucas)

The distinguishing of the five open-air species of British Earwigs is not a difficult matter.

It may reasonably be assumed that the common Earwig, Forficula auricularia, with which everyone has been familiar from childhood, can be recognised at sight. The specific characteristic to which attention must here be directed is the shape of the forceps. In the female these are parallel and almost touching throughout their length, in the male they are bowed. The broad basal part ends in a sharp point. The animal is from 10 to 14 mm. long.

Its congener, Forficula lesnei, is from 6 to 10 mm. long. The basal portion of the forceps is not pointed, but is smoothly rounded and the membranous wings do not visibly project beyond the wing-covers. It appears to be widespread in the south of England.

The largest Earwig, Labidura riparia, is at least 20 mm. long, or about twice the size of the common species. It is a pale buff colour and occurs only by the sea, usually on sand. In England it has been recorded, but rarely, from the neighbourhood of Bournemouth. It lurks under dry seaweed, just above high-tide mark.

The smallest Earwig, Labia minor, flies actively. The length of its body does not exceed 6 mm. and it is therefore easily distinguished from the others. It is of a yellowish colour and may be found flying on hot days, especially near heaps of manure. Its life-history is scarcely known.

In the species Apterygida albipennis the male forceps are separated at their bases and the points are slightly curved. The females are very like those of the common Forficula, but are narrower, paler and more hairy. The length of this species varies from 6 to 11 mm. It has occurred in the south-east of England.

Chapter XV

COCKROACHES

COCKROACHES, like earwigs, are primitive insects; indeed their fossil ancestors are remarkable for their large size and their resemblance to present-day species.

Most people, whether biologists or not, first come across these insects when they encounter the domestic "black beetle." This species is an immigrant, unable to live out of doors. It is said to have arrived in Britain at the beginning of the seventeenth century, making the voyage on merchant ships coming home from the East; but even Gilbert White, some 150 years later, looked upon it as "unusual." It was followed by a larger species, apparently coming from America, the species usually dissected in zoological laboratories.

General Appearance. Although the familiar Cockroach does not look like an earwig, or even like a large earwig, when examined superficially, it is found, on closer scrutiny, to be a very similarly constructed insect.

The Cockroach's head is a flattened pear-shape, bearing two large compound eyes and two long sensitive antennae, composed of many segments. The biting mouth-parts consisting of toothed mandibles, paired first maxillae and fused second maxillae are so like the corresponding appendages of the earwig that no further description is necessary. A comparison of Figs. 11 and 14 will show this, and will also show the unimportant ways in which the two insects differ. The head is joined to the thorax by a slender neck which is hidden by a projection of the first thoracic segment.

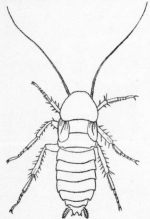

FIG. 13.—A Female Cockroach
(× 1)

Each segment of the thorax carries a pair of legs consisting of six pieces —coxa, trochanter, femur, tibia, metatarsus and tarsus. The femur and tibia are provided with bristles which the animal uses for cleaning its body and wings: the tarsus, which is itself five-jointed, ends in two curved claws, between which is an adhesive pad, the pulvillus or arolium, for climbing. The coxae are much longer than those of the earwig and are partly responsible for the surprising speed with which a Cockroach runs and the agility with which it avoids our attempts to tread on it.

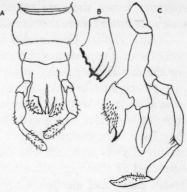

FIG. 14.—Mouth-parts of Blatta (× 10)
A Labium. *B* Mandible. *C* Maxilla

Wings are borne by the second and third segments of the thorax. The first pair are hard "horny" elytra such as are found in earwigs and beetles. They function as protective wing-covers and during flight are opened at right angles to the body, acting as stabilisers. It is but seldom that the domesticated Cockroaches fly at all. The second pair of wings are transparent and membranous; when not in use they are compactly folded under the elytra. Young Cockroaches have only rudimentary wings and this condition persists to maturity in the females of Blatta orientalis.

The abdomen consists of ten segments, each with hard tergite above and sternite below : the eighth and ninth segments, however, are telescoped and are not easily seen. The tenth sternite projects backwards and is deeply notched. It carries a pair of jointed cerci anales, and in the male the ninth segment has a pair of short styles as well. In the female the seventh sternite extends backwards into a boat-shaped genital pouch.

Life-History. The ovaries of the Cockroach consist of two sets of eight tubes, often very conspicuous when the insect is dissected. Sixteen eggs mature at the same time and are laid together in an egg-case or ootheca. This is a brown purse-like object which appears at the end of the female's abdomen and is visible in this position for some days before it is finally dropped. It is of no interest to its mother, who abandons it from the first.

The young ones which hatch from it in due course are paler than their parents and are wingless, but are quite obviously Cockroaches: hence they are called nymphs and not larvae. They moult six times before they are mature.

General Habits. Cockroaches are lovers of darkness, of crevices and of warmth; in consequence they live indoors, are hidden during the day and are active at night. They can be bred and reared in captivity, but for success in this their cage must be kept warm, even as must the water in aquaria of tropical fish. They are almost completely omnivorous, and their cast skins are usually eaten after they have been discarded; they are not cannibals but they will eat any of their comrades who die from other causes, and they are suspected of nibbling each other's wings. They are very fond of bread, sugar and alcohol. They are sensitive to changes in the moisture of the atmosphere and clearly possess a keen sense of smell, which leads them into traps baited with beer.

Economics. As pests of civilised man, Cockroaches are not to be compared with many other insects smaller than they. They do not carry dangerous bacteria, but they do destroy a quantity of food and since they often occur in very large numbers in surroundings which favour them this may be a serious loss. The removal of an old skirting board, for instance, often reveals in the space behind a clotted mass of Cockroaches, and food-containers, such as flour-bins or biscuit-boxes, if once accessible, may be found to be filled with Cockroaches instead of their original contents. In these circumstances they emit a characteristic and very unpleasant odour, which is quite unmistakeable and which may easily contaminate food which the insects have not actually spoilt by gnawing.

Increasing attention to public health, constant inspection and improved sprays and deterrents, aimed at insect and other pests have, however, affected Cockroaches, and many a bakery or hot-house which, a generation ago, was a well-populated vivarium is now almost as sterile as an operating theatre—and the livelihood of our exotic Orthoptera must be far more precarious than formerly.

Systematics. Cockroaches belong to the sub-order Dictyoptera of the order Orthoptera, which also includes the crickets, grass-hoppers and locusts. They are a large group, with several dozen European species. Three wild species only are true natives of Britain, but, as has been said, black beetles are only too common in most of the older houses of this country. Tropical species often arrive in crates of fruit and in other ways; some of these are well established in artificial conditions, but others, through frequent arrivals, have always failed to survive.

List of British Cockroaches

NATIVE

Ectobius lapponicus (L.)
Ectobius lividus (Fabr.)
Ectobius panzeri Steph.

IMMIGRANT

Blatta orientalis (L.)
Periplaneta americana (L.)
Periplaneta australasiae (Fabr.)
Blattella germanica (L.)
Pycnoscleus surinamensis (L.)

The three native species are superficially much alike. The smallest is Ectobius panzeri, about 6 mm. long and found on coastal sandhills. It does not seem to occur inland. Of the two larger species, E. lapponicus is darker and E. lividus is tawny: neither has so far been recorded north of the Thames. It is therefore obvious that for the experimental naturalist the imported species are likely to be the most useful, and indeed, domesticated as they are, they are well adapted to life in captivity.

The ordinary domestic black beetle is Blatta orientalis: it is not really black, but is a very dark red-brown, and it differs from true beetles (which may be black) in that its forewings might be loosely described as tough and leathery rather than hard and horny, and it undergoes no metamorphoses during its life.

The American Cockroach is larger and is a bright red-brown in colour; it is in fact a magnificent example of a lowly insect when it is examined without the prejudice that usually surrounds it. It is found only where artificial heating is continuous, as in the Zoological Gardens. The Australian Cockroach is similarly confined to warmed houses; it has a yellow band on the edges of its elytra, and a yellow spot on the pronotum or shield covering the first segment of the thorax.

The pronotum of Blattella germanica has two dark bands. This species is probably to be found in most large towns; in London restaurants it is aptly called the Shiner, in Lancashire it is the Steam Fly and in the U.S.A. the Croton Bug. At Kew Gardens and elsewhere Pycnoscleus surinamensis is established; it has a pale yellow streak on the elytra and its pronotum is shining black.

Chapter XVI

ANTS

AMONG Ants, and their relatives the bees and wasps, a social
life is more elaborately organised than in any other group of
the animal kingdom, with the result that the inner mysteries
of the beehive and ants' nest have for long been the subject of investigation. Although more is known about Ants than about some
of the other animals in this book, they are well worth the
naturalist's attention.

General Appearance. Ants are sharply distinguished from all
other insects by several features. These include the apparent addition of a fourth segment to the thorax, and the division of the
abdomen into two regions, a slender mobile "pedicel" and a larger
"gaster."

The head of an Ant is variable in shape. The antennae consist
of two parts, a longish basal segment, called the scape, and directly
joined to the head, and a distal segmented portion which consists
of ten to thirteen pieces. Ants have a pair of compound eyes
situated one on each side of the head; the number of facets to
each eye is sometimes as many as twelve hundred. In addition
there are often three simple eyes, one median and two lateral,
placed triangularly between the compound eyes. These eyes are
absent from the workers of some species.

The mouth-parts, adapted for biting, bear a close resemblance
to those of the earwigs and cockroaches. The mandibles are stout
and toothed; the first maxillae have each the same pair of lobes,
the lacinia and galea,
with the same maxillary
palp. The galea carries
a row of bristles, used by
the animal in cleaning
its legs. The pair of
second maxillae are
fused to form the labium,
which carries a tongue,
an organ not found in the

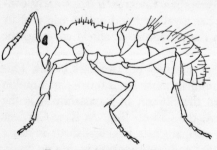

FIG. 15.—An Ant (× 8)

cockroaches. This tongue can be protruded; it has a roughened surface and with it the Ant can lick up its food and clean its body and the bodies of other Ants.

The first three segments of the Ant's thorax are the typical segments of this part of an insect. Each carries a pair of legs, and the second and third carry a pair of wings when these structures are present. The legs of Ants are remarkably uniform in all species and consist of the typical coxa, trochanter, femur and tibia, followed by a five-pieced tarsus bearing two claws. The two pairs of wings are both membranous, but worker Ants are wingless and the females lose them after the "marriage-flight."

The fourth thoracic segment or epinotum is the first abdominal segment of the larva, which, during pubation, becomes joined to the metathorax. It has no appendages. The abdomen is more highly specialised than in many insects. The narrow waist or pedicel, which joins the epinotum to the gaster, may be made of one or two segments, the second and third abdominal segments. The gaster itself consists of four or five segments in the worker or female and of five or six in the male, according to the number of segments included in the pedicel. The gaster may be round, oval or elongated. The last segment, called the pygidium, contains the reproductive organs and the sting, when this is present.

Life-History. The eggs laid by the queen Ant are quickly picked up by the workers and gathered into a heap. They are said to increase in size after they have been laid. They are objects of constant attention from the workers, who frequently lick them and are continually moving them about the nest. Some species systematically arrange eggs, larvae and pupae in groups, according to the state of their development, for the different stages need different conditions. Many of the eggs are eaten by the workers and the queen, and some are fed to recently-hatched young ones.

After a time that varies from a few days to some weeks, the eggs turn into larvae—small yellowish grubs, coated with hairs and quite helpless. These are fed by the workers on regurgitated food, varied with bits of egg and pieces of insects, until in time they change into pupae. The pupae are generally protected by a cocoon—they are, in fact, the "ants' eggs" of the goldfish bowl—and the cocoon is usually opened by the workers when the young ant, or "callow" as it is called, is ready for an active life. This generally occurs after two or three weeks in the pupal state. The callow is encumbered by the pupal skin, which is carefully stripped off it by the workers. If this is not completely done cripples will be produced.

The great event in the life of the Ant colony is the nuptial flight on which the females are fertilised by the males. As among bees, one impregnation supplies the female with sufficient sperm to fertilise the eggs she will lay during the rest of her life. The flight may occur at any time between May and October, and there is little doubt that different species respond to different atmospheric conditions, and that these conditions are an important factor in the choice of the moment. Many different colonies of a species spread over a wide area may choose the same time, and it is apparent that the workers, who control the event, choose the exact moment and prevent the males and females from leaving the nest too soon.

The males, unlike drone bees, do not die immediately, but they have now neither function in the life of the colony nor purpose in their own. They wander about and are soon killed and eaten.

The females have sometimes not flown very far, and may return to the nest in which they were reared, to assume the regal positions to which they are now promoted. Others may find their way to another colony, enter it and receive a royal welcome as valued additions to the strength of the tribe. Others again become the founders of new colonies, seeking the protection of suitable hiding-places in which to begin to lay their eggs.

In most cases the females now remove their wings, by pushing them with their legs or rubbing them against convenient obstacles. Inside the nest, the workers may help in the process. The females, however, are henceforward devoted to a single duty, which they perform with an efficiency and a prodigality which not many small animals can equal. They become, in effect, egg-factories. The workers supply them with food and continuously they convert their food into more Ants, laying as they do an egg every ten or fifteen minutes as long as the need for more Ants in the nest and its satellite nests is maintained. The life of a female Ant may last for sixteen years, giving a potentiality of half a million eggs.

Habits. Too much has been discovered about the habits of Ants to enable more than a very brief summary to be included here. The social organisation of the Ants' nest has reached such a pitch of elaboration that many naturalists have been attracted to its problems, and some writers have described Ants as reasoning beings, with personal characters not unlike those of man.

Three types or "phases" of individuals exist among Ants, males, females or queens and workers or wingless females. But many different modifications of these, both normal and abnormal, have been known to occur, and a descriptive list of twenty-nine of these has been given by Donisthorpe.

Male Ants are always winged; they are smaller and slenderer than the females and usually darker in colour. The female is the most highly specialised phase, with large head and thorax and swollen gaster. In some foreign species the queen is of a relatively enormous size compared with her workers. Her antennae, and in some species her wings, are shorter and stouter than those of the male. The workers, which are imperfect females, have a smaller thorax and no wings; their ocelli too are smaller and are often absent.

All the work of the colony is done by these workers, who tend the eggs and larvae, collect the pupae in groups and assist in the hatching of the young. It becomes quite apparent to anyone who keeps Ants under observation that they can distinguish friends from foes, and experiments have shown that recognition depends on the smell of the individual. Most myrmecologists agree that Ants are able to communicate with one another, conveying news of impending danger, of the finding of food or of circumstances where help is needed. The "speech" of Ants seems to consist of tapping movements with the antennae, pulling with the mandibles or butting with the head, and tapping the gaster on the ground. Attempts, not altogether unsuccessful, have been made to translate these actions so that a human being can, as it were, understand what the Ants are saying.

Some students of Ants are quite confident in granting these insects feelings and impulses, such as pleasure, fear and affection, and in seeing in their deeds evidence of memory and intelligence. It is this, combined with the ease with which a number of societies of different species of Ants can be kept under close observation, that makes them of unapproached interest and value to all who appreciate this branch of biology.

Systematics. Ants belong to the insect order Hymenoptera, characterised by the possession of four membranous wings. A sub-order, the Aculeata, includes Ants, bees and wasps, within which the Ants form the family Formicidae. The world-population of

Formicidae numbers many species, of which thirty-six species are generally recognised as British.

List of British Ants

Family Formicidae
  Sub-family Ponerinae
    Ponera coarctata (Latr.)
    Ponera punctatissima Roger
  Sub-family Myrmicinae
    Myrmicina graminicola (Latr.)
    Formicoxenus nitidulus (Nyl.)
    Anergates atratulus (Schenck)
    Monomorium pharaonis (L.)
    Solenopsis fugax (Latr.)
    Myrmica laevinodis Nyl.
    Myrmica ruginodis Nyl.
    Myrmica sulcinodis Nyl.
    Myrmica scabrinodis Nyl.
    Myrmica lobicornis Nyl.
    Myrmica schencki Em.
    Stenamma westwoodi (Steph.)
    Leptothorax clypeatus Mayr
    Leptothorax acervorum (Fabr.)
    Leptothorax nylanderi (Först.)
    Leptothorax corticalis (Schenck)
    Leptothorax tuberum (Fabr.)
    Leptothorax interruptus (Schenck)
    Tetramorium caespitum (L.)
  Sub-family Dolichoderinae
    Tapinoma erraticum (Latr.)
  Sub-family Formicinae
    Acanthomyops fuliginosus (Latr.)
    Acanthomyops niger (L.)
    Acanthomyops alienus (Först.)
    Acanthomyops brunneus (Latr.)
    Acanthomyops flavus (Fabr.)
    Acanthomyops umbratus (Nyl.)
    Acanthomyops mixtus (Nyl.)
    Formica rufa L.
    Formica pratensis Retz.

Formica exsecta Nyl.
Formica sanguinea Latr.
Formica fusca L.
Formica rufibarbis Fabr.
Formica picea Nyl.

A key for the determination of the identity of any British Ant would be a very elaborate and lengthy one, owing to the fact that males, females and workers need separate treatment. This would make such a table quite disproportionate to the rest of this little book and its omission is justified since all such keys are to be found in Donisthorpe's *British Ants,* an excellent and readily accessible book. Some help in the business of naming an Ant is to be obtained from the following key to the sub-families and genera of our native fauna.

1(2)	Pedicel unjointed, consisting of petiole only	3
2(1)	Pedicel of two distinct segments (Myrmicinae)	7
3(4)	Gaster constricted between segments i and ii (Ponerinae)	Ponera
4(3)	Gaster not constricted	5
5(6)	Gaster with five visible segments; anus circular (Formicinae)	23
6(5)	Gaster with four visible segments; anus a transverse slit (Dolichoderinae)	Tapinoma
7(8)	No sterile workers existing	Anergates
8(7)	Workers exist	9
9(10)	Antennae with ten segments	Solenopsis
10(9)	Antennae with more than ten segments	11
11(12)	Petiole quadrangular	Myrmicina
12(11)	Petiole not quadrangular	13
13(14)	Post-petiole with ventral spine	Formicoxenus
14(13)	Post-petiole without ventral spine	15
15(16)	Epinotum without spines	Monomorium
16(15)	Epinotum with two spines	17
17(18)	Last three segments of funiculus together shorter than the rest	Myrmica
18(17)	Last three segments scarcely shorter than the rest	19
19(20	Eyes small and inconspicuous	Stenamma
20(19)	Eyes normal	21
21(22)	Shoulders angular	Tetramorium
22(21)	Shoulders rounded	Leptothorax
23(24)	Frontal area triangular; eyes distinct	Formica
24(23)	Frontal area rounded posteriorly; eyes indistinct	Acanthomyops

Chapter XVII

DRAGONFLIES

THE Dragonfly appeals to the naturalist as essentially an insect of bright hours in warm sunshine; its fearsome name recalls memories of a flash of colour sweeping over the surface of a pond, flying with a speed and a precision which make it conspicuous—and very difficult to catch. A Dragonfly is indeed a lovely thing, and an entomologist can comfort himself when one of them eludes him with the thought that its colours are almost impossible to preserve.

General Appearance. A Dragonfly is in many ways remarkably built, with a large head, sloping thorax and long abdomen. The head carries two great compound eyes, some of which have been estimated to contain as many as twenty thousand separate lenses, and a group of three ocelli, or simple eyes, as well. The antennae are very short. The mouth-parts include a pair of powerful biting mandibles, comparable to those of the cockroach, and the maxillae are curiously modified to form a kind of cage or trap for the prey. The head is much more mobile than is usual among insects, for it is placed on a slender neck formed from the first segment of the thorax.

The two remaining segments are sloped forwards and downwards, an arrangement which has the result of bringing the legs close to the maxillae and carrying the wings back to lie along the abdomen. The legs are not well adapted for walking, but are used chiefly for seizing the prey. There are always two pairs of wings, very much alike in shape. They are transparent and glossy, very liberally provided with veins, especially in a transverse direction, and a characteristic of a Dragonfly's wing is a small notch or re-entrant angle on the fore-edge.

In relation to the rest of the body, the abdomen is one of the longest to be found among insects. It is composed of ten distinct segments and has a unique feature in that the male system opens on the second segment.

Life-History. The life of the Dragonfly is one of the most remarkable in natural history. The eggs are sometimes laid in gelat-

inous strings adhering to
objects under the water,
sometimes t h e y a r e
separately washed off the
female as, dipping her
abdomen, she flies close
to the surface, and by
some species they are
laid in the stems of
aquatic plants, the ovi-
positor cutting a small
groove to receive them. Some Zygoptera, or
damsel-flies, crawl beneath the water in order to
lay their eggs.

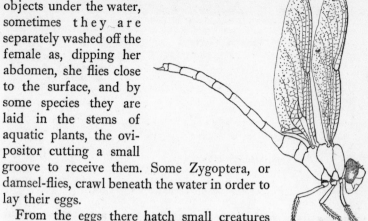

Fig. 16.—
A Dragonfly ($\times$ 1)

From the eggs there hatch small creatures
called pronymphs, covered completely in a transparent membrane from which they free themselves in a few minutes. The naiad or nymph
which emerges is a wholly aquatic and carnivorous animal, whose
youth and immaturity may last for less than a year but which, in
some species, may extend to five years. During this time it breathes
by gills, which in the Anisoptera are contained in the rectum and
in the Zygoptera are visible as caudal appendages. These external
gills are sometimes lost by accident, but the nymph seems to survive their loss. The gills are connected by tracheal tubes, which put
the internal organs in communication with the air. Usually these
nymphs crawl about the stems of aquatic plants, but Anisopteran
nymphs can squirt a jet of water from their so-called branchial
basket and thus shoot forwards by a primitive jet-propulsion.

Their food consists largely of mayfly larvae and mosquito
larvae, but they are not particular and tadpoles or small fish may
be captured. Their method of securing their food is unique. The
second maxilla or labium is extended into a long process, armed
at the tip with a pair of curved spines. Arising from behind the
mouth this labium is directed backwards, close to the lower side of
the thorax, then turns forwards and extends to the front of the
head, which it completely hides from below. For this reason it is
called the mask. On the approach of a possible victim the mask is
shot out with unbelievable speed and the prey transfixed by the
sharp spines.

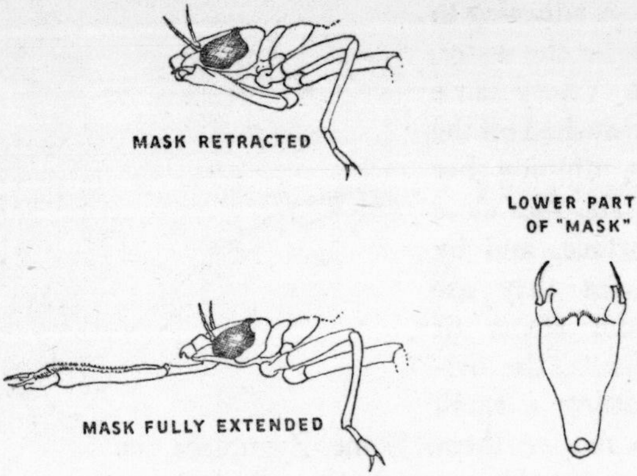
MASK RETRACTED
LOWER PART OF "MASK"
MASK FULLY EXTENDED

FIG. 17.—Mask of Dragonfly Larva (× 4)

During its nymphal life the Dragonfly moults twelve times, while its wing-cases become successively larger and more conspicuous. Finally it climbs out of the water, its last nymphal skin dries and cracks along the top of the thorax. The emerging thorax widens the split and the head is pulled out, followed by the legs and abdomen. The cast skin remains sticking to the hinder segments, but the animal bends its body, seizes the moult with its legs and frees itself from the encumbrance.

It is now weak and almost defenceless and is said to be in the teneral condition. Its wings quickly harden, enabling it to fly, but for a time it is very vulnerable. Some days pass before its adult colours appear.

General Habits. The strength and speed of the adult Dragonfly enables it not only to evade many human collectors but also to capture its prey on the wing with a hawk-like precision. The victim is seized in mid-air by the particularly spiny legs and pushed forwards to the mouth-parts. The great energy which it expends in its rapid flight results in a nearly insatiable appetite, and Dragonflies are in consequence extremely voracious, destroying enormous numbers of insects of many kinds. The Anisoptera are able to hover and even to fly backwards. Their activity, like that of birds, demands a high temperature, but whereas the heat of a bird's body is derived from within, that of a Dragonfly is largely dependent on external sunshine. Hence they occupy the glades of woods but not the shade of the trees and are to be seen on the hedgerows of sunny lanes and especially on the banks of

The new dragonfly with wings now fully expanded and dry.

Culex larvæ hanging from the water surface.

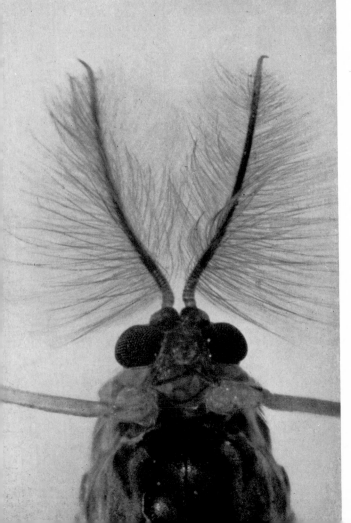

Mosquito. Head of a male showing the characteristic antennæ.

streams and the edges of ponds. Also like a bird, an individual Dragonfly often occupies a limited territory; it makes periodic flights over much the same paths and frequently returns to rest on the same plant or branch from which it set out on its raid.

At its greatest the speed of a Dragonfly has been estimated at 60 m.p.h., and the insects are able to migrate in large swarms over very considerable distances.

Economics. Although in days gone by Dragonflies have been supposed to be dangerous, and have even been given the name of "horse-stingers," they do no harm at all to men or to any large animal. Their nymphs do no appreciable harm to fish-breeders and the adults do not specialise in attacks on any valued insects. They have therefore but little economic importance.

Systematic. Dragonflies belong to the order of insects known as Odonata. This is divisible into a sub-order Zygoptera, or damsel-flies, and a sub-order Anisoptera, or Dragonflies. The forty-three British species belong to nine families.

List of British Dragonflies

Sub-order Zygoptera
    Family Agriidae
        Agrion virgo (L.)
        Agrion splendens (Harris)
    Family Lestidae
        Lestes sponsa (Hansemann)
        Lestes dryas Kirby
    Family Platycnemididae
        Platycnemis pennipes (Pallas)
    Family Coenagriidae
        Pyrrhosoma nymphula (Sulzer)
        Ischnura elegans (Linden)
        Ischnura pumilis (Charpentier)
        Enallagma cyathigerum (Charpentier)
        Coenagrion puella (L.)
        Coenagrion pulchellum (Linden)
        Coenagrion mercuriale (Charpentier)
        Coenagrion hastulatum (Charpentier)
        Coenagrion armatum (Charpentier)
        Coenagrion scitulum (Rambur)
        Erythromma najas (Hansemann)

Ceriagrion tenellum (Villers)
Sub-order Anisoptera
Family Gomphidae
Gomphus vulgatissimus (L.)
Family Cordulegasteridae
Cordulegaster boltoni (Donovan)
Family Aeschnidae
Brachytron pratense (Müller)
Aeschna cyanea (Müller)
Aeschna juncea (L.)
Aeschna grandis (L.)
Aeschna caerulea (Ström)
Aeschna mixta Latreille
Aeschna isosceles (Müller)
Anax imperator Leach
Family Corduliidae
Cordulia aenea (L.)
Somatochlora metallica (Linden)
Somatochlora arctica (Zetterstedt)
Oxygastra curtisi (Dale)
Family Libellulidae
Orthetrum coerulescens (Fabricius)
Orthetrum cancellatum (L.)
Libellula quadrimaculata L.
Libellula depressa L.
Libellula fulva Müller
Sympetrum striolatum (Charpentier)
Sympetrum vulgatum (L.)
Sympetrum sanguineum (Müller)
Sympetrum fonscolombii (Selys)
Sympetrum flaveolum (L.)
Sympetrum danae (Sulzer)
Leucorrhinia dubia (Linden)

A key to separate this multitude might be a very long affair. A shortened form is here given and the puzzled student is advised to consult the very full version in Miss Longfield's book. (See p. 76.)

1(2)	Body stout; eyes contiguous	3
2(1)	Body slender; eyes separated	51
3(4)	Abdomen longer than wings; large insects	5
4(3)	Abdomen shorter than wings; small or medium	21

5(6) Thorax not very hairy; hind wings very broad at base   7

6(5) Thorax very hairy; base of hind wings not very
                                broad   Brachytron pratense

7(8) Eyes touching over some distance; body not yellow and
                                    black 9

8(7) Eyes only just touch; body black and yellow
                              Cordulegaster boltoni

9(10) Abdomen brown   11

10(9) Abdomen with blue, green or yellow spots   13

11(12) Thorax brown with plain yellow lateral bands
                            Aeschna isosceles

12(11) Thorax with blue spots; yellow lateral bands
                  with brown edges   Aeschna grandis

13(14) Lateral thoracic stripes narrow or absent   15

14(13) Lateral thoracic stripes broad and continuous   17

15(16) Thorax bright green   Anax imperator

16(15) Thorax brown   Aeschna caerulea

17(18) Thorax brown, unstriped   19

18(17) Thorax brown with two green or yellow stripes Aeschna cyanea

19(20) Face yellow, unlined   Aeschna mixta

20(19) Face crossed by black lines   Aeschna juncea

21(22) Abdomen broad and flat; insect stout   23

22(21) Abdomen narrow; insect slender   29

23(24) Brown; all wings with black spot at top
                       Libellula quadrimaculata

24(23) Wings unspotted at top centre   25

25(26) All wings with dark brown patch at base   Libellula depressa

26(25) Wings wholly clear or patch only to posterior pair   27

27(28) Wings wholly clear   Orthetrum cancellatum

28(27) Posterior wings with dark brown patch at base   Libellula fulva

29(30) Male abdomen of uniform width   31

30(29) Male abdomen constricted at third segment   39

31(32) Male blue   Orthetrum coerulescens

32(31) Male red or black and red   33

33(34) Female yellow-brown, with few black marks   35

34(33) Female yellow and black equally   Leucorrhinia dubia

35(36) Black streaks on 8th and 9th abdominal segments   37

36(35) No such streaks   Sympetrum striolatum

37(38) Abdomen black beneath   Sympetrum flaveolum

38(37) Abdomen not black beneath   Sympetrum fons columbii

39(40) Green   43

40(39) Not green   41

41(42) Male black; female black and yellow   Sympetrum danae

42(41) Male red; female yellow   Sympetrum sanguineum

43(44)	Eyes separated	Gomphus vulgatissimus
44(43)	Eyes touching	45
45(46)	Abdomen green with yellow spots	Oxygastra curtisi
46(45)	Abdomen unspotted green	47
47(48)	Yellow nose and face	49
48(47)	Yellow on nose but not on face	Cordulia aenea
49(50)	Yellow on sides of face joining below nose	
		Somatochlora metallica
50(49)	Yellow spot on each side of nose	Somatochlora arctica
51(52)	Blue or green	53
52(51)	Neither blue nor green	61
53(54)	Wings dark or coloured	55
54(53)	Wings clear	57
55(56)	Veins at base of wings very dense	Agrion virgo
56(55)	Veins here no denser than elsewhere	Agrion splendens
57(58)	Metallic patch on first abdominal segment rounded	
	at top corners	Lestes sponsa
58(57)	This patch square at top corners	Lestes dryas
59(60)	Red or bronze	61
60(59)	Neither red nor bronze	65
61(62)	Crimson stripes on male thorax; nose hairy	
		Pyrrhosoma nymphula
62(61)	No such stripes; nose smooth	Ceriagrion tenellum
63(64)	Abdomen greenish black	65
64(63)	Abdomen blue	69
65(66)	Blue spot near each eye	67
66(65)	No blue spot near eye	Erythromma najas
67(68)	Segment viii of abdomen blue	Ischnura elegans
68(67)	Segments viii and ix of abdomen blue	Ischnura pumilis
69(70)	Blue spot near each eye	71
70(69)	Blue line joining eyes	Platycnemis pennipes
71(72)	Thorax blue with black stripes; one black stripe on	
	each side	Enallagma cyathigerum
72(71)	Thorax black; two black stripes on sides	73
73(74)	Male with very long anal appendages	Coenagrion armatum
74(73)	Male with all anal appendages very short	75
75(76)	Black U-mark on segment ii	77
76(75)	Segment ii otherwise marked	79
77(78)	U-mark thick at base	Coenagrion pulchellum
78(77)	U-mark thin at base	Coenagrion puella
79(80)	Segment ix with narrow blue ring	Coenagrion mercuriale
80(79)	Segment ix half blue or more	81
81(82)	Segment ix half blue	Coenagrion scitulum
82(81)	Segment ix all blue	Coenagrion hastulatum

Chapter XVIII

MOSQUITOES

GNATS have been evening pests to men and women for many a century, and since the First World War the possibility that a chance Mosquito bite might infect the victim with malaria has increased the general respect for these insects. A great deal of research has been carried out on the habits and characters of Mosquitoes in all parts of the world, and the British representatives form a group which many amateur entomologists may find attractive.

General Appearance. A Mosquito presents to the casual observer the appearance of a delicately-built fly, with two wings, like the common house-fly, with rather long legs and, most important, a long, piercing proboscis.

The head carries two large compound eyes and a pair of "feathery" antennae, between which the proboscis is centrally visible. In the formidable genus Anopheles, the palpi, one on each side of the proboscis, are very conspicuous, for they are as long as the proboscis and so give to members of the genus the appearance of having a triple organ. Actually, when the insect is feeding these palpi are extended forwards. In the other British genera they are too short to be easily noticed and the proboscis looks single.

On the thorax there are three pairs of legs which are much longer than the insect's body and are thin and delicate. The capture of a Mosquito is very likely to injure them, damage which should be avoided when possible, since the presence or absence of pale rings, especially on the last or tarsal segments of the legs of the third pair is of

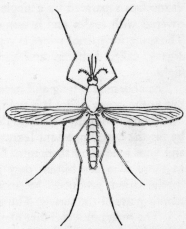

Fig. 18.—A Mosquito (× 4)

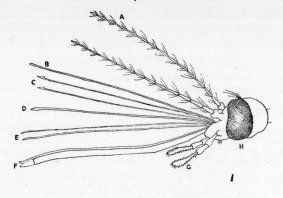

A = ANTENNAE	E = PAIRED MAXILLAE
B = LABRUM	F = LABIUM
C = PAIRED MANDIBLES	G = MAXILLARY PALPI
D = HYPOPHARYNX	H = COMPOUND EYE

FIG. 19.—Mouth-parts of Anopheles ($\times$ 12)

importance in identifying it. The tarsi of a Mosquito have five parts or segments; in some species these are wholly dark, in some there is a white or pale yellow band at each end and in some a pale band only at the proximal, or upper, end of a segment. The fifth segment ends in a pair of claws.

The wings are characteristic. They represent the anterior pair, and the group can be distinguished by the existence of two large veins which divide into two not far from the wing-tip, and are themselves separated by a single simple vein. Also, the veins are covered with scales and in some species the wings are spotted. The posterior pair of wings is represented by short drumstick-like organs, called halteres, and used as balancers or stabilisers in flight.

The abdomen is long and narrow; it is usually blunt at the tip, but in the genus Aëdes it is pointed.

Although not fully visible to the naked eye, the mouth-parts are by far the most important feature in the structure of a Mosquito, and some account of them must be given. Apart from their interest to those who are bitten, they provide an example of extreme specialisation produced by modification of the simple biting mouth-parts of the earwig. The parts may be analysed as follows:

i. The mandibles and first maxillae have the form of four long, pointed stylets, the main piercing organs.

ii. Accompanying them into the skin of the victim is a fifth lancet, a projection from the floor of the mouth, known as the hypopharynx. In this is a duct from the salivary glands; the saliva is injected into the wound, prevents the blood from clotting (and may carry in the malarial parasites, if any).

iii. As well as these five organs, a tube made from the labrum (or upper lip) and partly from a projection from the roof of the mouth, known as the epipharynx, enters the wound and the blood is sucked up it into the stomach.

iv. All these parts lie in a protecting sheath, which is the labium or second maxillae, its sides curved upwards so that only a narrow slit runs along the upper surface. At its tip are two flaps or lobes, the labellae.

When the Mosquito bites, these labellae are placed against the skin and all the enclosed parts pierce the skin easily. The labium itself does not do so, but curves outwards behind the group of stylets. The body of Culex remains almost horizontal as this happens, but the body of Anopheles rises at the posterior end.

Life-History. Mosquitoes lay their eggs on water, where they float singly or in little groups called rafts. About twenty eggs are laid at a time. They are only about a millimetre long, and in a few days they hatch, opening downwards as the larva within pushes its way out. The eggs of Aëdes are laid on moist ground.

The larvae are aquatic, like the larvae of dragonflies, mayflies, caddisflies and others, and they are often to be seen in water-butts as well as in ponds and marshes. They breathe ordinary air, with which they make contact through the terminal tube or respiratory syphon at the end of the abdomen; they are thus hanging from the water surface-film, larvae of Culex being almost vertical, those of

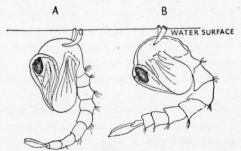

Fig. 20 (*a*).—Pupae of Culex (*A*) and Anopheles (*B*) (× 6)

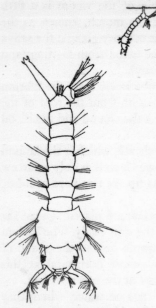

Anopheles more nearly horizontal. Their constantly moving limbs waft a current of water into their mouths, so that, like a mussel and many other water-dwellers, they feed on whatever digestible particles the water may chance to bring.

They grow quickly in warm conditions and as larvae moult three times as their size increases. At the fourth moult they become pupae, peculiarly shaped objects, much like a comma, with a large almost spherical anterior part and a segmented abdomen. The pupa has two short breathing tubes near its "head." It does not feed at all, but unlike many larvae it is a moderately active creature; if startled it drops from the surface and then quickly wriggles its way upwards again.

FIG. 20 (b).—Larva of Culex (× 8)

Not many pupae are as active as this, for they are in general a resting form in which all the organs of the adult are being reproduced inside the body.

After some three to five days the pupal skin splits along the back and the young adult climbs out of the water to commence its aerial life.

General Habits. Mosquitoes, as everyone knows, are insects which are most often seen flying about in swarms, sometimes in immense numbers, in the warm hours of the evening. They seldom seem to travel, but content themselves with apparently pointless activity in the same place. To this general impression there are, of course, a few exceptions. Several British species are active and may bite at any time of the day, and a few, notably Aëdes caspius, may attack us even in our houses some miles from their breeding-grounds.

It is also well known that male Mosquitoes are vegetarians, feeding on the sap of plants, and that the enemies of man, cattle and even frogs are the females.

The various species of British Mosquitoes differ from each other

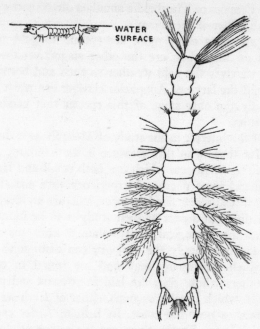

WATER SURFACE

FIG. 20 (*c*).—Larva of Anopheles (×8)

in fertility and in hibernation methods. Some species lay all their eggs within a few days in the early summer; others may produce a later brood, so that their larvae are found perhaps in June and again in August; and a few, such as Anopheles plumbeus, may deposit three batches of eggs in a year.

There is also diversity in the way in which the winter is passed and the species survives until the spring. In the genus Aëdes the well-protected eggs are laid in the ground and are very resistant to both cold and drought, and it is the rule for this genus to hibernate in the egg stage. In Anopheles maculipennis the males and late larvae usually die in the autumn, but adult females pass the winter indoors, in stables, cowsheds or pigsties. Usually they are almost inactive, but the variety atroparvus is not so, and may take an occasional meal at any season. The same is true of Culex pipiens, the females of which are to be found on the ceilings of our cellars throughout the winter and spring, feeding very occasionally and waiting until the warmth of May before they emerge and lay their eggs. Females of Theobaldia annulata often share cellars and stables with either of the above.

Larvae are in general more susceptible to cold and more dependent on food than are the other stages, yet the larva of Mansonia survives the cold weather as such and becomes adult in May; and the larva of Anopheles claviger can resist frost and is apparently the only stage of this species that persists in the winter months.

Much of the interest in the study of Mosquitoes is due to their delicacy; for those who take pleasure in the handling, mounting and examining of insects which are both small and fragile, and which demand some degree of experience, care and skill in the laboratory, Mosquitoes, like false-scorpions, are an ideal subject.

A quite different aspect of their study is to be found in their very interesting ecological distribution. Within the structural limits of a single family the ecologist can distinguish domestic species, which accompany man and are found in towns and villages; others whose eggs are laid in streams and pools; and others again which inhabit swamps, either of fresh water inland or salt marshes near the coast. In Britain, Aëdes caspius is a typical brine-lover. Lastly, there are the rather original species which lay their eggs in water-filled hollows on the branches of trees, and of which the adults are to be found in woods and parks.

Economics. There is little need to stress the economic importance of mosquitoes, which are responsible for the spreading of malaria, yellow fever and elephantiasis. These diseases are rare in Britain, but cases of malaria due to Anopheles maculipennis are reported from time to time. Apart from this, Mosquitoes have a very considerable "nuisance value" and at some times and in some places may make outdoor life a misery, even to the extent of affecting the popularity of a seaside resort.

Fortunately the methods of control are now well established. Opportunities for laying eggs in water can be diminished by removing or covering small containers, marshes can be drained, lakes and ponds can be stocked with fish which will eat larvae and pupae, and these can also be suffocated by the addition of oil to the water. This spreads over the surface and prevents the insects from breathing. The result is that, given sufficient labour and leadership an area can be cleared of Mosquitoes and the diseases they spread can be reduced to small proportions.

Systematics. In the order of two-winged flies there is included a family of blood-suckers, known as the Culicidae, which is divided into three sub-families, Culicinae, Dixinae and Chaoborinae. The Gnats and Mosquitoes with which this chapter is concerned belong to the first of these and number at least twenty-eight species contained in six genera.

List of British Mosquitoes

Sub-family Culicinae
> Anopheles maculipennis Mg.
> Anopheles claviger Mg.
> Anopheles algeriensis Theo.
> Anopheles plumbeus Steph.
> Aëdes caspius Pall.
> Aëdes dorsalis Mg.
> Aëdes flavescens Müller
> Aëdes annulipes Mg.
> Aëdes cantans Mg.
> Aëdes rusticus Rossi
> Aëdes communis Degeer
> Aëdes leucomelas Mg.
> Aëdes detritus Hal.
> Aëdes punctor Kirby
> Aëdes sticticus Mg.
> Aëdes geniculatus Oliv.
> Aëdes vexans Mg.
> Aëdes cinereus Mg.
> Theobaldia annulata Schrank
> Theobaldia subochrea Edw.
> Theobaldia alaskaensis Ludlow
> Theobaldia morsitans Theo.
> Theobaldia litorea Shute
> Theobaldia fumipennis Steph.
> Orthopodomyia pulchripalpis Rond.
> Mansonia richiardi Fic.
> Culex pipiens L.
> Culex apicalis Adams

Even the elementary biology books of to-day include an account of the several differences between Anopheles, which might conceivably be carrying malaria, and Culex, which does not; but it is to be seen from the above list that there is more in the identifying of a British mosquito than that. A microscope is a very great help, if not an absolute necessity, and the points to which attention is chiefly to be directed are the length of the palpi, the shape, blunt or pointed, of the abdomen, and the presence or absence of rings on the tarsal segments of the legs, and of spots on the wings.

The following key will be of some help in naming the commoner species; eleven rarer ones are omitted. The student may consult Dr. Marshall's book mentioned on page 76.

1(2)	Proboscis apparently trifid; abdomen without scales or white marks (Anopheles)	3
2(1)	Proboscis obviously single; abdomen with scales, some of them white	9
3(4)	Without white tuft on forehead; brown Anopheles algeriensis	
4(3)	With white tuft on forehead	5
5(6)	Small; black with broad grey stripe on back	
		Anopheles plumbeus
6(5)	Larger; brown	7
7(8)	With spots on wings	Anopheles maculipennis
8(7)	Without spots on wings	Anopheles claviger
9(10)	Abdomen pointed in female; legs i and ii with pectinate claws (Aëdes)	11
10(9)	Abdomen blunt; tarsal claws smooth	27
11(12)	Legs with pale rings, especially on tarsi	13
12(11)	Legs without rings	19
13(14)	Rings on both ends of tarsal segments	Aëdes caspius
14(13)	Rings only on proximal, upper, ends of segments	15
15(16)	Thorax and abdomen dark brown or blackish Aëdes cantans	
16(15)	Thorax light brown or reddish	17
17(18)	Abdomen yellow	Aëdes flavescens
18(17)	Abdomen brown with yellow bands	Aëdes annulipes
19(20)	Abdomen with 5 or 6 complete transverse white bands	21
20(19)	Abdomen without transverse bands	25
21(22)	Wings with scattered white scales	Aëdes detritus
22(21)	Wings without such white scales	23
23(24)	Large; median longitudinal yellow line on abdomen	
		Aëdes rusticus
24(23)	Small; abdomen brown	Aëdes punctor
25(26)	Blackish; silvery-white knee-spots	Aëdes geniculatus
26(25)	Thorax reddish; abdomen dark	Aëdes cinereus
27(28)	Larva and pupa subaquatic	Mansonia richiardi

28(27) Larva and pupa of normal habits 29
29(30) Larva with four or five pairs of hair tufts on breathing-tube
Culex pipiens
30(29) Larva with one pair of tufts at base of breathing-tube
(Theobaldia) 31
31(32) Wings with spots; legs with white rings   Theobaldia annulata
32(31) Wings unspotted; rings pale and indistinct
Theobaldia morsitans

A few notes on some of the above species may be of help and interest.

In most parts of Britain the commonest indoor Mosquito is the well-known Culex pipiens. There are two or three generations of this gnat in a year and it becomes most numerous in the autumn. Females alone survive the winter, hibernating in cellars. It is not a serious pest of man, whom it seldom bites, preferring birds or frogs.

Anopheles maculipennis is the vector of malaria, which it very occasionally causes in Britain. Its bite is not painful and is usually given in the evening and indoors; its chief victims are cattle. Anopheles claviger is also common; it hibernates in the larval stage and seldom enters houses. The bite of Anopheles plumbeus is often painful and is followed by swelling, and human beings may be bitten during the day as well as in the evening, and either in or out of doors.

The only British Aëdes which enters houses is Ae. caspius. This species winters in the egg stage; the adults often fly a considerable distance and are a regularly occurring nuisance in London. The other species of the genus seldom fly far, but most of them are troublesome biters near their breeding-places, and Ae. cinereus will bite during the daytime.

In the genus Theobaldia only one species is really important; this is T. annulata, the largest British Mosquito and one of the largest in the world. It has two broods in a year, and bites both men and animals freely at dusk. Its bite is usually painful and most of the accounts of serious inflammation following a Mosquito-bite are to be attributed to this species. It is a very common species, but does not seem to spread any parasitic disease.

Chapter XIX

CENTIPEDES

THE familiar word Myriapoda, formerly the name of a class of Arthropoda, is becoming obsolescent, and to use it is to confess oneself old-fashioned. Like the group Invertebrata and like, more recently, the class Pisces, it has disintegrated as more detailed study of its components has laid more and more emphasis on their differences. As a result the class Myriapoda is to-day replaced by the class Chilopoda, or the Centipedes, and the class Diplopoda, or Millipedes; and the resemblances between them are ascribed to convergent or parallel evolution.

General Appearance. There is, perhaps, no animal in which the segmental character of the body of an invertebrate is more obvious than in the Centipede. The head, which appears to constitute the first segment, is really composed, like the head of an insect, of several segments coalesced. It carries a pair of eyes, when eyes are present, a pair of antennae, and the mouth-parts.

The eyes are simple smooth ocelli: the antennae are mobile, pointed sensory organs of many segments, which systematists sometimes have to count.

The mouth-parts consist, like those of insects, of a pair of mandibles and two pairs of maxillae. The mandibles are hard unbranched pieces, well provided with teeth; the first maxillae are fused together to form a median lobed plate; the second maxillae are like small legs in appearance, but they are used in feeding, and the basal segment of each has a small blunt process known as a gnathobase.

Behind the head is the first segment of the body or trunk, known as the basilar segment. Its appendages are known as maxillipeds; they are poison-claws, at the tips of which open the ducts from a pair of venom-glands contained in the segment. The proximal part of the limb is prolonged into a

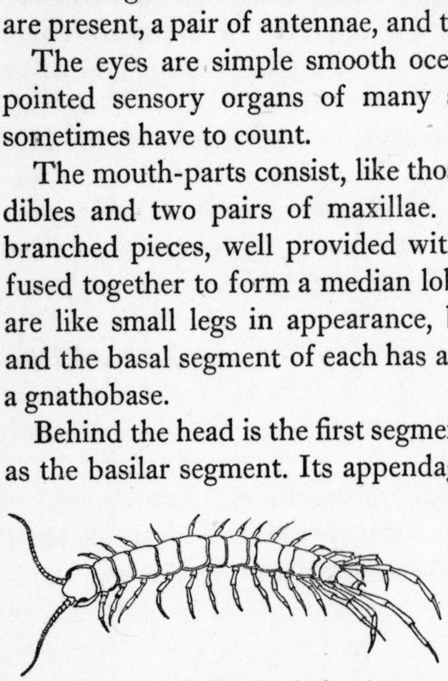

FIG. 21.—A Centipede (× 1)

strong gnathobase by which the prey is held while poison is injected into it.

The remainder of the body of a Centipede is composed of similar segments, varying in number from fifteen, as in the common brown Lithobius, to 173. Each segment is a flattened ring of hard chitin, and each bears one pair of legs. The legs consist of seven segments and end in a hooked claw; those of the last segment are usually larger than the rest.

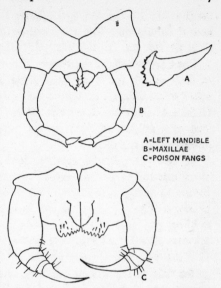

A=LEFT MANDIBLE
B=MAXILLAE
C=POISON FANGS

FIG. 22.—Mouth-parts of Lithobius (× 10)

Life-History. Centipedes in Britain lay their eggs in the spring or summer, fertilised by sperm which may have been received during the previous autumn. The oviducts open on the lower surface of the last segment, and by convulsive wrigglings of the tail-end of the animal the egg is expelled and grasped by two small hooks, designed to receive it. It is sticky and is at once rolled in the earth until it is indistinguishable from a particle of soil. This apparently helps to protect it from other Centipedes who would readily eat it. The mother then abandons it. In some families the female lays 15 to 30 eggs in a loose mass, while in others a degree of maternal care exists.

The young Centipede that hatches from the egg has at first its venomous maxillipeds and at least six pairs of legs. As it grows new segments appear between the last and the penultimate segments until the full complement is reached.

FIG. 23.—
Last Segment of
Lithobius (× 10)

General Habits. Centipedes avoid the light and are usually to be found in the same kind of situation as are the Woodlice described elsewhere in this book, wherever there is darkness, moisture, protection and food. One common and one rare species live by the sea and appear to be able to survive several hours' immersion, but they are in no sense marine or aquatic animals. Several species are habitual cave-dwellers.

They are wholly carnivorous, and are rapid movers, very active in their search for insects and their larvae, slugs and worms and other small animals on which they prey. Even flies sometimes fall victims to their sudden swift darts. Their bite is comparable to that of a spider, efficient for its purpose but only exceptionally dangerous to man.

At least three British species, Scolioplanes crassipes, Geophilus electricus and G. carpophagus, have the unusual property of being luminous at night, the result of a phosphorescent fluid which they produce. The secretion of the fluid may be produced by gently tickling the animal or by suddenly immersing it in water; it appears also if the Centipede is attacked by ants or other enemies. It is more frequently seen in the autumn, the season when Centipedes tend to leave their burrows, and probably it is a mere reflex response to certain stimuli and the light-production is incidental. It has no sexual significance, for the luminous species are also blind.

Systematics. The British Centipedes fall into three orders, easily separated:

Lithobiomorpha: 15 body-segments.
Scolopendromorpha: 22 body-segments.
Geophilomorpha: 31–173 body-segments.

List of British Centipedes
Order Lithobiomorpha
    Lithobius piceus L.K.
    Lithobius agilis C.L.K.
    Lithobius lapidicola Meinert
    Lithobius borealis Meinert
    Lithobius calcaratus C.L.K.
    Lithobius pilicornis Newport
    Lithobius muticus C.L.K.
    Lithobius forficatus (L.)
    Lithobius variegatus Leach
    Lithobius nigrifrons Latzel
    Lithobius melanops Newport
    Lithobius crassipes L.K.

Millipede. A species from Tanganyika.

A centipede (*Scolopendra morsitans*).

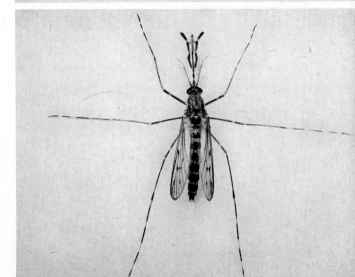

Common mosquito (*Theobaldia annulata*).

Millipede (*Polymicrodon*) constructing its "tent" in preparation for skin-changing.

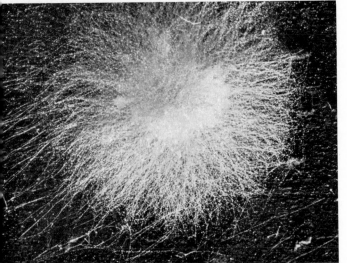

The finished "tent".

Female millipede coiled around her eggs.

Lithobius duboscqui Brölemann
Lithobius curtipes C.L.K.
Lamyctes fulvicornis Meinert
Scutigera coleptrata (L.)
Order Geophilomorpha
Haplophilus subterraneus (Shaw)
Stigmatogaster gracilis (Meinert)
Mecistocephalus carniolensis (C.L.K.)
Hydroschendyla submarina (Grube)
Schendyla nemorensis (C.L.K.)
Schendyla zonalis
Chaetechelyne montana Meinert
Chaetechelyne vesuviana (Newport)
Scolioplanes maritimus (Leach)
Scolioplanes acuminatus (Leach)
Scolioplanes crassipes (C.L.K.)
Clinopodes linearis (C.L.K.)
Necrophlaeophagus longicornis (Leach)
Geophilus carpophagus Leach
Geophilus insculptus Attems
Geophilus electricus (L.)
Geophilus algarum Brölemann
Geophilus fulcorum
Geophilus scillyensis
Brachygeophilus truncorum (Bergsoe)
Order Scolopendromorpha
Cryptops hortensis Leach
Cryptops anomolans Newport

There is at present no generally available key for the separation of these animals.

Chapter XX

HARVESTMEN

SINCE the order of Spiders is excluded from the present book because there are nearly six hundred species found in Britain, the Harvestmen take their place as familiar and typical representatives of the class Arachnida. They form an order known as the Opiliones or Phalangidea, of which the world contains upwards of two thousand different kinds; there are three sub-orders and all the twenty-one British species are contained in one of these, the Palpatores.

General Appearance. The Harvestman's body has not the thin waist which, in spiders as in insects, separates the abdomen from the parts in front of it; it has a smooth oval outline, the cephalothorax and abdomen being joined across their whole breadth. The cephalothorax is composed of six segments and carries the six pairs of appendages —chelicerae, pedipalpi

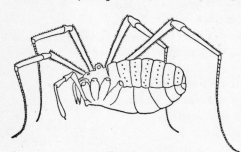

FIG. 24.—A Harvestman (× 3)

and four legs—common to all orders of the Arachnida. It is separated from the abdomen by a fairly deep groove. The latter consists of ten visibly distinct segments, but their distinction, marked by transverse grooves or rows of small spicules, is not always easy to make out. Moreover a general distortion of the body has occurred, so that the upper plate or tergite of any one segment is not necessarily vertically above its own lower plate or sternite.

The carapace covering the cephalothorax carries the eyes. In Harvestmen the eyes are seldom set in the surface, but are borne on the sides of an eye-turret, or ocular tubercle, which rises near the middle of the fore-edge. Thus they stare sideways, like the eyes of a bird or a fish. Their surfaces, as in spider's eyes, are smooth.

At the sides of the eye-turret, near the second pair of legs, there

are the openings of a pair of odoriferous glands; the glands themselves can in some species be seen through the carapace, looking
like another pair of eyes.

On the underside of the Harvestman's body the basal segments
of the legs, or coxae, almost meet in the middle, so that there is no
sternum or breastplate, such as exists in spiders. From the front of
the abdomen there projects forwards a hard flat plate, the genital
operculum, the shape of which needs sometimes to be noted.

Spines or pointed tubercles and bristles or setae of various
lengths and shapes are freely scattered over a Harvestman's body
and limbs. There is usually a double row of them along the centre
of the eye-turret and in some genera an important group of three
such tubercles forms a trident in the middle of the fore-edge of

Fig. 25.—Chelicera of
Phalangium (× 8)

Fig. 26.—Pedipalp of
Oligolphus (× 8)

the cephalothorax. This trident is often useful in determining a
species.

The appendages or limbs of a Harvestman are the chelicerae,
the pedipalpi and the legs. The chelicerae or jaws are of three
segments: the third works against a pointed prolongation of the
second and so forms an organ like a crab's claw on a small scale.
The chelicerae are the Harvestman's only weapons and they are
not venomous.

The pedipalpi are short leg-like limbs: they are chiefly sensory
organs for use in contact with objects close to the body, and they
also help in grasping the food and bringing it to the jaws. In some
genera they end in a claw, in others they do not, and in the former
case the claw may be smooth or toothed.

The legs are eight in number, and in all the British species the
second pair are the longest. The others are habitually used for
walking, but the second pair are usually stretched out in front,
feeling the ground and clearly acting in somewhat the same way as

do the antennae of insects. The legs are of seven segments, and the last, the tarsus, is often divided into a number of pieces, giving it great flexibility. It ends in a smooth claw.

Life-History. The females lay their eggs in clumps of thirty or more in damp earth, and if it is desired to raise a second generation in captivity a pan of fine soil kept well moistened should be included in the cage. If it is not, the eggs will be laid in the drinking-water. Eggs that are laid, as most of them are, in August or September hatch in February or March if kept indoors: it is probable that in the open they develop more slowly than this. A few species pass the winter as young or as adults.

There is no larval stage and the nymphs are from the first just like their parents. They moult for the first time within an hour of emerging from the egg; later in life they cast their skins about every ten days until they are mature. In moulting, they hang themselves up by the legs of the fourth pair, wriggle out of the split skin of their bodies and then slowly pull their long legs from their old cases. Their chelicerae help in this and the bundle of legs emerges and lengthens until it is bent into a large circle, when suddenly a released leg shoots out like a spring uncoiling.

There is much to be learnt about the individual differences in the life-histories and habits of the various species.

General Habits. Harvestmen are to be found in woods and hedges throughout the spring and summer. In the autumn they become much more conspicuous and may often be seen running across open meadows or along the roads, or resting, sometimes in bright sunshine, on the walls of houses or the trunks of trees. Occasionally they are found in groups of twenty, forty or fifty specimens, but they are in no real sense social animals. In the winter they are under fallen leaves and are best found by sifting, and at all times they are more numerous in damp surroundings, such as ditches and the edges of ponds.

They are essentially nocturnal animals, and when kept in cages are found to be quiescent during most of the day. They shun the light and rest in the darker corners until evening. Then they awake, eat, drink and wander about, generally indifferent to each other save when they meet one of the opposite sex. Even in captivity they mate freely and instantaneously, with none of the courtship and none of the tragedy that characterise the lives of spiders.

Their food is very varied, and enthusiasts who have watched them out of doors at night by the light of electric torches have reported them as consumers of many kinds of smaller creatures. An interesting detail, which distinguishes them both from spiders and from false-scorpions, is that they do not limit themselves to living prey. In cages they will eat bread and butter, meat and fat, and always they drink much water. If well fed they are very seldom cannibals.

When in difficulties, Harvestmen have two methods of self-defence. The glands already mentioned as present in the head can secrete an odorous fluid which, presumably, is nauseous to some of the Harvestman's enemies. Among most British species the odour seems to be almost imperceptible to human noses, but there is no doubt of its existence, and in some foreign species it is distinct enough.

Alternatively, a Harvestman which has been seized by a leg easily sheds the leg and escapes on the rest. This method is of course familiar among spiders and several other Arthropoda, where the lost limb is usually regenerated below the exo-skeleton and appears at the next moult. A peculiarity of Harvestmen is that they do not regenerate the limbs they have lost, and as autumn advances the number of individuals with fewer than eight legs distinctly increases. One famous book has recorded the finding of a Harvestman that ran easily on two legs only. Another peculiarity is the way in which a separated leg continues to twitch in spasms for some while after it has been shed. Some naturalists have seen in this a device to occupy the attention of the predator and to delay it while the former owner of the leg escapes. Whether this is so or not, it is a remarkable experience to come across an isolated leg lying on the ground and kicking all by itself!

Systematics. Harvestmen belong to the class Arachnida in which they constitute the order Opiliones or Phalangidea. There are upwards of two thousand known species, divided among three sub-orders. All the British species belong to the sub-order Palpatores, and are found in three of its six families.

List of British Harvestmen

Family Trogulidae
    Trogulus tricarinatus L.
    Anelasmocephalus cambridgei (Westwood)

Family Nemastomatidae
 Nemastoma lugubre (Müller)
 Nemastoma chrysomelas (Herm)
Family Phalangiidae
 Homalenotus quadridentatus (Cuvier)
 Leiobunum rotundum (Latr.)
 Leiobunum blackwalli Meade
 Nelima silvatica (Simon)
 Phalangium opilio L.
 Opilio parietinus (Degeer)
 Opilio saxatilis (C. L. Koch)
 Megabunus diadema (Fabric.)
 Platybunus triangularis (Herbst)
 Oligolophus agrestis (Meade)
 Oligolophus tridens (C. L. Koch)
 Oligolophus hanseni (Kraep.)
 Oligolophus meadei Cambr.
 Odiellus spinosus (Bosc.)
 Odiellus palpinalis (Herbst)
 Mitopus morio (Fabric.)
 Lacinius ephippiatus (C. L. Koch)

Harvestmen are easy to identify and many species in the above list can be recognised at sight.

The two members of the Trogulidae are not very common, and can be distinguished by the mask of setae which rises from the fore-edge of the cephalothorax and hides the mouth-parts. Also the eyes lie flat on its surface and not on an ocularium.

Nemastoma lugubre and Homalenotus quadridentatus have characteristic patterns. The former is black with two white spots, the latter is brown, with three rows of square dark spots.

The genus Leiobunum has a tiny round body and disproportionately long legs; L. rotundum has a black ring round its eyes, and L. blackwalli a white ring.

Of the rest, Phalangium opilio is the common brown species of autumn. It is pure white underneath and the male has very prominent chelicerae. The two species of Opilio replace it later in the year; they are speckled greyish animals, with dark spots on the coxae. Platybunus triangularis is the only British species common in the spring, and Megabunus diadema is unmistakable because of the very long spines on the ocularium. Mitopus morio is probably the commonest and most widespread British Harvestman; its body has a dark mark above, somewhat in the shape of an hour-glass. In Lacinius ephippiatus this mark on the back has straight sides and is squarely cut off just in front of the hind edge of the abdomen.

The genera Oligolophus and Odiellus, which are closely related, have a trident of three spines in front of the eye-turret. O. agrestis and O. tridens are very common; Odiellus spinosus is easy to recognise by its large flat body and relatively short legs.

The British species can be separated by the following key:

1(4)   Cephalothorax with bifurcated hood; eyes level
with surface of carapace (Trogulidae)   2

2(3)   Hood of large semicircular plates, with small
tubercles on outer edge   Trogulus tricarinatus

3(2)   Hood of small projections with long cylindrical
tubercles   Anelasmocephalus cambridgei

4(1)   No such hood; eyes raised on ocularium   5

5(8)   Tarsus of pedipalp without claw (Nemastomatidae)   6

6(7)   Body black with two white spots; pedipalpi of normal
length   Nemastoma lugubre

7(6)   Body yellow-brown; pedipalpi much longer than
body   Nemastoma chrysomelas

8(5)   Tarsus of pedipalp with claw (Phalangiidae)   9

9(16)   Palpal claw toothed   10

10(11) Abdomen with four posterior tubercles
Homalenotus quadridentatus

11(10) Abdomen smooth posteriorly; legs extremely long   12

12(15) Ocular tubercle smooth; trochanters dark; coxae without
dark spot   13

13(14) Black ring round eyes   Leiobunum rotundum

14(13) White ring round eyes   Leiobunum blackwalli

15(12) Ocular tubercle with two rows of spines; trochanters
pale; coxae with dark spot   Nelima silvatica

16(9)   Palpal claw smooth   17

17(32) First segment of chelicerae with ventral spur; ante-
ocular region with trident of three spines   18

18(23) Femora of palpi with ventral spines or teeth   19

19(20) Femora and tibiae of legs strongly toothed
Lacinius ephippiatus

20(19) Femora and tibiae of legs only hairy   21

21(22) Body broad and flat; trident spines almost horizontal
Odiellus spinosus

22(21) Trident spines erect or nearly; central spine slightly
the longest   Odiellus palpinalis

23(18) Femora of palpi ventrally only hairy   24

24(25) Fore-edge of carapace with trident of small tubercles;
legs long   Mitopus morio

25(24) Fore-edge of carapace with trident of sharp spines; legs
not very long   26

26(27) Central spine of trident twice as long as the others;
setae on tarsi long   Oligolophus meadei

27(26) Central spine of trident equal to or slightly longer than
the others   28

28(29) Central spine slightly in advance of the others; genital
plate with anterior notch   Oligolophus agrestis

29(28) Spines of trident in straight line   30

30(31) Angular femora; light colour   Oligolophus tridens

31(30) Cylindrical femora; dark colour   Oligolophus hanseni

32(17) No spur on chelicerae; no trident on carapace   33

33(36) Tibial segment of palp with apophysis   34

34(35) Ocular tubercle with two rows of five long spines
Megabunus diadema

35(34) Ocular tubercle with normal spines   Platybunus triangularis

36(33) Tibial segment of palp unbranched   37

37(38) Brown species with dark central mark; second segment
of male chelicera with horn   Phalangium opilio

38(37) Grey species   39

39(40) About 8 mm. long; abdomen with median band or row
of whitish spots   Opilio parietinus

40(39) About 5 mm. long; abdomen with inconspicuous median
line   Opilio saxatilis

Chapter XXI

FALSE-SCORPIONS

LIKE the Harvestmen described in the preceding chapter, the False-scorpions are an order of the class Arachnida. Their proper name is either Pseudoscorpiones, Chelonethi or Chernetes. They are much less conspicuous than either Harvestmen or Spiders; in fact they are not always easy to find even when they are specially sought, and many good field-naturalists pass years without ever seeing them.

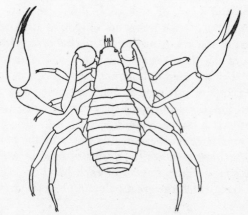

FIG. 27.—A False-scorpion (× 20)

General Appearance. A False-scorpion has neither neck nor waist, indeed its shape is very much like that of a true Scorpion without its tail. Its cephalothorax is covered by a generally smooth carapace, in which the eyes are set. There may be two eyes or four, but the ten members of the genus Chernes are blind. The lenses of the eyes are smooth, as in Harvestmen and Spiders. The abdomen is always fully segmented; there are twelve segments in all, quite clearly distinguished by eleven separate transverse plates or tergites above and ten or eleven sternites below. The twelfth pair of plates are joined and make a terminal ring, there being no arching active tail with its formidable sting. The apparent loss of

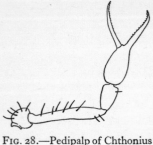

FIG. 28.—Pedipalp of Chthonius
(× 20)

one sternite is due to the fact that the first and second sternites may be fused together, forming a genital plate.

These and other details can be distinguished only with the help of a lens or microscope, for the largest False-scorpion in the world is little more than a quarter of an inch long, and our native species range between 1·1 mm. and 3·6 mm. In consequence they are not as terrible as their sinister name implies: they are venomous, but they are not strong enough to pierce human skin.

The limbs or appendages in front of the legs consist of a pair of chelicerae and a pair of pedipalpi. The former are very small, and are made up of two segments only, one working against a prolongation of the other, just as in the chelicerae of harvestmen. Some authors call these organs the hands of the animal, and not inaptly, for they are used to hold and carry pieces of food, to pick up the small bits of grit used in building nests, and to clean the other limbs. For these purposes they are provided with two important features. First, each contains a silk-secreting gland which opens at a spinneret on the movable finger of the hand, and the silk is used to bind together the grains of sand of which the nest is made. Secondly, both fingers of each hand are supplied with combs, between which the great palpi and legs are drawn in order to clean them.

Just behind the chelicerae are the great pedipalpi, the weapons of the False-scorpion. These are limbs of six segments, and the last two are arranged like the last two segments in the great claw of a lobster, that is to say the last segment opens and shuts against a projection from the last but one. There are poison-glands inside one or both of these fingers, opening at a sharp tooth just inside the tip. Whatever its nature, and I do not think that it has ever been analysed, it seems to be very virulent: I have seen a False-scorpion bite a spider considerably larger than itself and kill it instantaneously. These great organs are obviously very important in the life of a False-scorpion and they are of great interest to the microscopist who can see how very variable are their proportions in different species. They may be slender or relatively stout, and the forceps may be long or short, straight or curved, and so on, so that it is probably true to say that the pedipalp of each species is different from those of all other species and is a distinguishable feature of the animal that possesses it.

FIG. 29.—Leg of Neobisium (× 20)

The legs of False-scorpions may be described as short, shorter even than the legs of spiders. Their first segments, or coxae, meet in the middle line of the lower surface of the cephalothorax, so that there is no sternum, or at the most a rudimentary one. The coxae give no help in crushing the food, in which respect they differ from the coxae of both scorpions and harvestmen. The legs are made of eight segments in all, and they end in a pair of sharp claws with a "sucker" between them. The legs of the third and fourth pairs are generally stouter than those of the first and second pairs.

Chelicerae, pedipalpi and legs are all bearers of long hair-like setae, which are usually supposed to act as very delicate organs of touch. Those on the pedipalpi are twelve in number and are always arranged according to the same plan or to slight modifications of it, and there is little doubt that the efficient working of these setae, and also of other sense-organs on the limbs, depends on their cleanliness. This explains the care with which a False-scorpion brushes its legs and palpi with its chelicerae.

Life-History. The eggs of False-scorpions are laid in the summer, a curious contrast to the habit of most Arachnida, which lay in autumn. Each female lays only one lot of eggs each year, and probably only once in her life. The eggs are delivered from the oviduct into a special incubation chamber, or brood-pouch secreted beforehand to receive them; it has the shape of an inverted mushroom, its stalk still attached to the oviduct and the eggs, varying in number from 7 to 40, occupying the circular part.

When the eggs hatch, the young nymphs attach themselves by their mouth-parts to their mother's oviducal orifice and nourish themselves by sucking a secretion, "uterine milk," from her. As a result she becomes very emaciated, until after a moult, they leave the pouch. For a while the young remain on their mother's body, until their legs and pedipalpi have hardened, but after two or three days they leave her. If she is one of the species that spins a nesting-chamber, she makes a hole in this, large enough to enable them to crawl out.

General Habits. False-scorpions are nocturnal and are securely hidden in the daytime; they belong indeed to the division of animals described as cryptozoic, for although more active at night they are not necessarily more exposed. Many live under the bark of trees, when this is loose; yet the bark of dead trees, which is most easily removed by the collector, very seldom covers them. Débris in hollow tree-stumps and among the leaves of bracken may contain them, and ditches filled with fallen oak or beech leaves are nearly always inhabited by the genus Chthonius. These are the easiest to find, for they may readily be sifted from the leaves if the latter are dry; to wet leaves False-scorpions cling with a remarkable obstinacy.

Since they are so small and so hard to see against their natural backgrounds, their habits have almost all been learnt from captive specimens. They are easy to keep, and since they are not normally very cannibalistic a number may be kept together in a crystallising dish. A piece of moist filter paper on the bottom of the dish keeps the atmosphere humid and makes the animals more easily seen. It should never be allowed to dry.

False-scorpions may be fed on small insects of many sorts, such as may be sifted from leaves. Like many venomous animals they will not eat dead material, but they readily seize and quickly kill creatures like spring-tails and dipterous flies. These they consume completely, leaving nothing, even of the hard chitin.

Normally they walk slowly about, with an air of extreme deliberation, their large pedipalpi held stretched out in front and no doubt serving, like the antennae of insects, as essential sense-organs. They react to slight disturbances by withdrawing their pedipalpi and crouching motionless for half a minute or more; but to more formidable encounters they respond by running very rapidly backwards. This is a very characteristic habit and when they are thus darting away, with their palpi closely folded, they do not look like False-scorpions at all.

False-scorpions indulge in a type of courtship which though less elaborate than that of spiders is remarkable enough and is of interest because the animals are apparently in no danger from one another. Hence the usual "explanation" of the courtship of spiders, that it saves the male from the murdering female, cannot be advanced. When a male False-scorpion approaches a female, he retracts his palpi and vibrates or shakes his abdomen rapidly from side to side. The peculiar ram's-horn organs then appear, extended from beneath, as if in some form of "display." An unreceptive female waves a palp at her suitor and walks away; at other times she waves her palpi and vibrates her abdomen in response. The male then seizes her chelicerae in his, and for some time they remain thus clasped together, their forelegs occasionally waving about, their abdomens shaking.

The male then lowers his abdomen to the ground and draws out a viscous drop of fluid which hardens into a vertical rod with a spermatophore on top, like the head of a pin. He leads the female over this, so that it penetrates her orifice, shakes her vigorously so that the tip is broken off, and then leaves her.

There is considerable variation in the courtship behaviour of different species, and males, like some male spiders, often "make mistakes" and begin their courtship movements when they approach other males or young members or even members of a different species.

In some species the females construct nests from pieces of grit, held together with silk secreted by glands in their chelicerae. Other species do not seem to take this precaution, but produce their brood-pouch in any convenient shelter.

Young False-scorpions moult three times before becoming adult and they may live for two years or longer.

Systematics. The two dozen species of British False-scorpions may conveniently be arranged in six families.

List of British False-scorpions

Family Chthoniidae
    Chthonius halberti Kew
    Chthonius ischnocheles (Herm.)
    Chthonius orthodactylus (Leach)
    Chthonius tenuis L. Koch
    Chthonius tetrachelatus (Preys.)
Family Ideoroncidae
    Ideoroncus cambridgei (L. Koch)
Family Cheiridiidae
    Cheiridium museorum (Leach)

Family Obisiidae
    Neobisium muscorum (Leach)
    Neobisium carpenteri (Kew)
    Neobisium maritimum (Leach)
    Roncus lubricus (L. Koch)
Family Cheliferidae
    Dactylochelifer latreillei (Leach)
    Chelifer cancroides (L.)
    Withins subruber (Simon)
Family Chernetidae
    Chernes cimicoides (Fabr.)
    Chernes godfreyi Kew
    Chernes chyzeri (Tom.)
    Chernes dubius (Cambr.)
    Chernes powelli Kew
    Chernes panzeri C. Koch
    Lamprochernes nodosus (Schr.)
    Pselapochernes scorpioides (Herm.)
    Allochernes wideri (C. Koch)
    Dendrochernes cyrneus (L. Koch)

A survey of this list of two dozen species brings out the following helpful facts:

Two species, Ch. halberti and N. carpenteri, have been found, though rarely, in Ireland and the ordinary collector here may neglect them. Two species, L. nodosus and Ch. godfreyi, are frequently fly-borne, and more likely to be found on the legs of flies than elsewhere. L. nodosus is much the commoner: flies have of course carried it all over Britain, and four other species are also very widely distributed and are likely to be among the first captures—N. muscorum, Ch. ischnocheles, Ch. tetrachelatus and C. panzeri. Finally, two more species are usually found indoors, Ch. museorum and Chelifer cancroides.

In attempting to identify a British False-scorpion a microscope is almost essential. One looks first to see if the tergites of the abdomen are medially divided or not, then at the number of the eyes, if any, and then at such other details as are included in the key below. Of these the most difficult to determine is the presence or absence of the galea or spinneret at the tip of the movable finger of the chelicera.

The following table may be used to name a False-scorpion.

1(2)	Abdominal tergites without median division	3
2(1)	Abdominal tergites with median division	17
3(4)	Two eyes	5
4(3)	Four eyes	7
5(6)	Chelicera without galea	Roncus lubricus
6(5)	Chelicera with galea	Ideoroncus cambridgei
7(8)	First tarsus of one segment (Chthonidae)	9
8(7)	First tarsus of two segments (Obisiidae)	15
9(10)	Cephalothorax much wider in front than behind	
		Chthonius ischnocheles
10(9)	Cephalothorax not or scarcely wider in front	11
11(12)	Forceps of pedipalp curved	Chthonius tenuis
12(11)	Forceps of pedipalp straight	13
13(14)	Forceps of pedipalp only slightly longer than bulb	
		Chthonius tetrachelatus
14(13)	Forceps of pedipalp clearly longer than bulb	
		Chthonius orthodactylus
15(16)	Forceps of pedipalp much longer than bulb	
		Neobisium muscorum
16(15)	Forceps of pedipalp equal to bulb	Neobisium maritimum
17(18)	No eyes (Chernetidae)	25
18(17)	Two eyes	19
19(20)	Eyes placed far back	Cheiridium museorum
20(19)	Eyes near fore-edge of carapace	21
21(22)	Pedipalpi with long bulb and short forceps	Withius subruber
22(21)	Pedipalpal proportions normal	23
23(24)	Indoor species, up to 3·2 mm.	Chelifer cancroides
24(23)	Outdoor, littoral, sp: 2·9 mm.	Dactylochelifer latreillei
25(26)	Large species, over 3·5 mm.	Dendrochernes cyrneus
26(25)	Less than 3 mm.	27
27(28)	Small, less than 2 mm., fly-borne	Lamprochernes nodosus
28(27)	Normal size 2–3 mm.	29
29(30)	Pedipalpi with swollen bulb and rough surface	
		Chernes cimicoides
30(29)	Pedipalpi normal	31
31(32)	Cephalothorax covered with granulations	
		Pselapochernes scorpioides
32(31)	Cephalothorax smooth	33
33(34)	Setae club-shaped	Chernes dubius
34(33)	Setae normal, pointed	Chernes panzeri

Half-a-dozen rare or local species are omitted.

Chapter XXII

SLUGS

SLUGS are a good example of animals which, because of their retiring nature and nocturnal habits, are present almost everywhere in numbers which are quite unsuspected by the ordinary owner of a garden. Although they are usually thought to be both slimy and unattractive, they are really able to illustrate many of the phenomena of natural history.

General Appearance. Slugs differ from the snails to which they are allied in having no spirally coiled hump of viscera on their

Fig. 30.—A Slug(× 1)

backs. They resemble snails in having a pair of eye-bearing tentacles protruding from their heads and retractable at will. Close to these tentacles are two small lobes or lips which carry organs of taste. The upper surface of the body is in part covered by the mantle, which in snails secretes the protective shell. In Slugs the shell is reduced to a vestigial oval plate, which is visible on the outside of the body in one family, the Testacellidae; in the rest it is internal and can be found only by dissection. In some it is still further reduced and is represented only by a layer of chalky granules.

The reproductive orifice and the respiratory opening into the "lung" or pulmonary cavity is usually to be seen on the right side of the mantle.

The body behind the mantle may be described as the tail. The upper surface of the tail may carry a median ridge, called the keel, which may be conspicuous from mantle to tail-tip or may be inconspicuous and confined to the posterior part, or may be absent altogether.

The lower surface of a Slug is the foot, the sticky or slimy pad

Slug, with tentacles
retracted.

Common slug (*Arion
ater*).

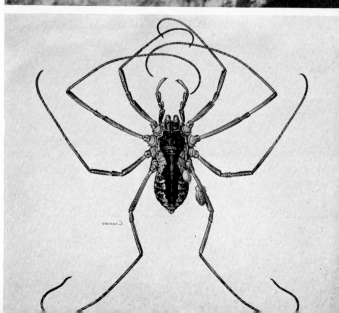

Harvestman (*Mitopus
morio*), one of the com-
monest British species.

Slug laying eggs.

on which it moves. If a Slug is watched from below as it crawls up a sheet of glass, the foot can be seen to be divided longitudinally into a median and two lateral regions, and that successive waves pass forwards along the median area, producing the movement of the animal.

The stickiness or sliminess of a Slug is due to a glandular secretion which in the absence of a shell protects the animal from desiccation. The skin of a Slug is able to retain a quantity of water for the same purpose, but even so Slugs are confined to a moist environment and in dry conditions shrink very considerably. Thus the "length" of a species is a somewhat variable measurement, depending on circumstances. In some Slugs the slime is coloured by red or yellow pigment; in others it is milky owing to grains of chalk.

Life-History. Slugs are hermaphroditic, as are snails, and mutual cross-fertilisation between two individuals is the rule. The eggs are laid underground near the surface of the soil, so that frequent disturbance of the top layer with the hoe, exposing the eggs and causing them to dry up, is a useful method of control.

Slugs mate at all times of the year, some on the open ground, some under any slight shelter, some underground. A remarkable form of courtship exists, in which two Slugs, secreting slime copiously, follow one another in a circle, like animals in a circus, except that the radius of their track gets gradually smaller. This continues for an hour or more, until mating occurs. The most surprising behaviour is that of Limax maximus, which mates in mid-air. The preliminary circling takes place on the foliage of a tree, until the two Slugs drop on a thread of slime which is strong enough to support them. In this awkward situation the exchange of sperm takes place.

General Habits. Slugs are so thoroughly nocturnal in their ways that the very occasional specimens seen crawling about on damp days give a completely false impression of the numbers that exist almost everywhere. It seems that their time of greatest activity begins two or three hours after sunset and that different species choose different times at which to "come out." They are active at all times of the year, but cold weather below freezing-point and drought keep them underground. Prolonged drought is fatal to more Slugs than is prolonged frost; this is because crawling over dry surfaces uses up their slime more quickly than it can be replaced. Although moisture in general is welcome, Slugs dislike actual rain, and they also dislike wind.

Their choice of food is very wide. The species of Testacella are purely carnivorous and eat chiefly earthworms and other small creatures, but the rest are practically omnivorous. They eat almost everything that a garden may contain, whether it be plant or animal, alive or dead, fresh or stale, pleasant or nauseating, and do so quite indiscriminately, simply taking, like locusts, what lies before them. One of the earliest accounts of the diet of Arion is that written by Dr. A. H. Cooke, whose list of substances eaten concludes with the words ". . . and Pear's soap, the latter reluctantly." Dr. Barnes has pointed out that the Slugs in a well-tended lettuce-bed will find nothing to eat except lettuce, those in a neglected one will proportionately satisfy their appetites on weeds, and spare the lettuces.

Economics. There is no denying that because of their omnivorous habit Slugs eat a proportion of the fruits and vegetables which we cultivate for our own use. In one garden alone, Barnes has estimated the weight of material consumed by Slugs in a year to be 1½ hundredweight, but it must be remembered that this is 180 lb. of Slugs' food and that not all of it was intended or was fit for human consumption. It is often thought to be locally desirable to attempt a control or reduction of the Slug population; and the success that may attend such efforts may be estimated from the same authority's remark that from one garden he removed between ten and seventeen thousand Slugs a year for four consecutive years and made no noticeable reduction in their numbers. The conclusion seems to be that the Slug, like the rabbit, is able to meet all the efforts which at present man thinks it worth his while to make in destroying it.

Systematics. Slugs belong to the order Pulmonata of the phylum Mollusca; they are therefore relations of the common snail. They are of great biological interest because they are not a homogeneous natural group with a single origin, but a group derived by degeneration of the shell from at least three different shell-bearing ancestors. Hence their general similarity is an example of convergent evolution. The identification of Slugs is not easy because nearly all species show a wide range of variation in size and especially in colour, and in some cases certainty can be reached only after dissection. The key which follows is probably adequate for typical adult specimens, but in use it should be supplemented by the fuller descriptions given in Dr. H. E. Quick's *Synopsis on Slugs*. (See page 75.)

List of British Slugs

    Family Testacellidae
        Testacella maugei Férussac
        Testacella haliotidea Draparnaud
        Testacella scutulum Sowerby
    Family Arionidae
        Geomalacus maculosus Allman
        Arion intermedius Normand
        Arion circumscriptus Johnston
        Arion hortensis Férussac
        Arion subfuscus (Draparnaud)
        Arion ater (L.)
        Arion rufus (L.)
    Family Limacidae
        Milax gagates (Draparnaud)
        Milax sowerbyi (Férussac)
        Milax gracilis (Leydig)
        Limax tenellus Nilsson
        Limax cinereo-niger Wolf
        Limax maximus L.
        Limax flavus L.
        Limax arborum Chantereaux
        Agriolimax agrestis (L.)
        Agriolimax reticulatus (Müller)
        Agriolimax laevis (Müller)
        Agriolimax caruanae Pollonera

IMMIGRANTS

    Limax valentianus Férussac
    Limax nyctelius Bourguignat

1(2) Mantle posterior, with external shell (Testacellidae)   3
2(1) Mantle anterior, shell internal   7
3(4) Dorsal grooves join near the mantle; no dorsal tubercles
                        Testacella scutulum
4(3) Dorsal grooves originate separately; dorsal tubercles present 5
5(6) Dorsal grooves originate far apart   Testacella maugei
6(5) Dorsal grooves originate close together   Testacella haliotidea
7(8) Respiratory pore anterior to middle of mantle; no keel
      (Arionidae)   9

8(7) Respiratory pore posterior to middle of mantle; keel
present (Limacidae)   21

9(10) Body marbled with yellow and white spots; Ireland only
Geomalacus maculosus

10(9) Body with lateral bands, not spotted (Arion)   11

11(12) Not more than 2 cm. long; body tubercles with conical points
Arion intermedius

12(11) More than 2 cm. long   13

13(18) Less than 10 cm. long   14

14(15) Sole orange; mucus orange   Arion hortensis

15(14) Sole not orange   16

16(17) Sole yellowish white   Arion subfuscus

17(16) Sole opaque clear white   Arion circumscriptus

18(13) More than 10 cm. long   19

19(20) Generally black or grey   Arion ater

20(19) Generally red or yellow   Arion rufus

21(22) Mantle divided by horseshoe into lateral and central
areas; median area of foot with chevron-like grooves;
keel from mantle to tip (Milax)   25

22(21) Mantle with concentric rings or ridges; keel on tail-tip
only   23

23(24) Posterior edge of mantle smoothly rounded (Agriolimax) 29

24(23) Posterior edge of mantle an obtuse angle (Limax)   31

25(26) About 7 to 7·5 cm. long   Milax sowerbyi

26(25) About 5 cm. long   27

27(28) Usually black with very dark keel   Milax gagates

28(27) Usually yellow or brown with orange keel   Milax gracilis

29(30) About 3·5 cm.; usually light-grey or brown; chalky slime
Agriolimax reticulatus

30(29) About 1·7 cm.; brown; paler mantle and sole
Agriolimax laevis

31(32) Pale blue tentacles   Limax flavus

32(31) Tentacles not pale blue   33

33(34) Smaller species, less than 5 cm. long   35

34(33) Larger species, 10 to 30 cm. long   37

35(36) Mucus yellowish   Limax tenellus

36(35) Mucus clear and stringy   Limax arborum

37(38) Generally black; black marks on sole; mantle spotted
Limax maximus

38(37) Generally black; pale sole; mantle banded Limax cinereo-niger

Chapter XXIII

OTHER POSSIBILITIES

THERE is, of course, no necessity that the group chosen for specialisation should have only a few British species. The reader, for instance, may already feel an attraction towards moths or beetles or spiders, all of which are represented in Britain by many more species than fifty. Yet the appeal of specialisation may also be strong.

In such a case it would be possible to adopt a limited portion of the chosen group. For example, among beetles the "ladybirds" might be selected; or among spiders the wolf-spiders or the crab-spiders. Study and collection among the whole group could be carried on in a general way, providing a background of related and comparative facts against which the smaller group would be more thoroughly investigated from the point of view of structure, behaviour, distribution and so on.

Again, it may occasionally be best to limit from the start the time that is to be devoted to the special group. I have in mind the case of a naturalist who one sunny morning in summer was un-expectedly fascinated by the variety of two-winged flies that were buzzing round the flowers on a clump of fertile ivy. He was quickly warned that the British Diptera are at least 5,000 in num-ber, but nevertheless he set about their study undaunted but with the reservation that he would not devote more than three years to them. He did this, and acquired a very sound knowledge of the two-winged flies of Britain, and also obtained at the same time a great deal of pleasure. At the end of his three years he turned with equal unexpectedness to the study of mosses, and zoology knew him no more. But the really disproportionate progress he had made in three years as a dipterologist was abundant proof of the success that may follow a confined or restricted effort.

This leads to a mention of another aspect of specialisation which constitutes perhaps its chief disadvantage. It is the ever-present temptation to refrain from learning anything about another animal or group of animals because to do so will take some effort or energy which might otherwise have been devoted to the special subject. I could quote as an example of a rather extreme case that of a botanist known to me whose devotion to the family of grasses was of this exclusive type. He could name any grass, wild or cultivated, to be found in Britain, and many from overseas as well, yet he was unable to recognise the Herb Robert, Deadnettle, Campion or Germander Speedwell close to which his grasses were growing. It may well be emphasised that the more effort a naturalist makes to learn about other organisms than his own, the more effort he will be able to make in connexion with the latter; while the wider his knowledge of biology in general the more clearly he will see the significance of his own discoveries.

In the preceding chapters twelve groups of invertebrates have been chosen because they were suitable for the treatment and kind of study which this book tries to suggest; but of course there are others, and a very brief mention of some of these will constitute our last suggestion to the would-be student of small animals.

Leeches. Leeches are animals which are not as well appreciated now as a century ago, when they were universally used by surgeons, but they are creatures that are easy to keep and interesting to watch. They are allied to the earthworms and form an order, Hirudinea, of the phylum Annelida. Eleven species of freshwater Leeches occur in Britain, and although the best-known, Hirudo medicinalis, the ordinary medicinal Leech, is now very scarce and perhaps extinct, some of the others are not rare. They may be found in streams and ponds or even dug up from the ground, and the writer can state that a bathe in the Cam is often an effective way of finding, or being found by, some of them.

Leeches have a segmented body always composed of thirty-four segments, but the outwardly visible rings are more numerous. The majority have a "sucker" at each end and the body is remarkably elastic, able to stretch out to three or four times its shortest length. Many of them are extremely beautiful animals, which move gracefully, either looping like caterpillars or swimming freely with rhythmical undulations. They live satisfactorily in an aquarium, but tend to leave the water and fix themselves an inch or two above its surface. In this situation their bodies are always damp, like those of earthworms.

A full meal is said to last a Leech six months or more, so that the biologist, even if he feeds them himself, will not find his charges to be a great tax. They may be fed on fresh blood from a slaughter-house, placed in their water in a stout linen bag.

Leeches may live for fifteen years and are said not to mate until they are six or seven. They are hermaphrodites, like earthworms, and like earthworms they lay eggs in a cocoon secreted as a ring round the body. The cocoon is attached to a water-plant or buried in the mud; it contains up to twenty eggs, which hatch as minute Leeches no thicker than pack thread.

Millipedes. Millipedes or Diplopoda will be found by anyone who looks for earthworms, centipedes, slugs or woodlice. Their rather distant relationship to the centipedes has already been mentioned. The body of a Millipede is more rounded than that of a centipede, the head has no poison-fangs, and each segment after the fourth has two pairs of legs. All Millipedes are vegetarians, and the spotted Snake-millipede, Blaniulus guttulatus, is often reported to have attacked sugar-beet, strawberries, potatoes and other crops. Another well-known species is the Pill-millipede, Glomeris marginata, which rolls itself up into a ball and is often mistaken for a woodlouse, but the usual method of protection among Millipedes is the emission of an unpleasant-smelling fluid from a pair of special stink-glands.

Millipedes are easy to keep in cages, which should have a layer of earth on the bottom: their food should be sliced apple, chopped leaves and grass. The eggs are laid in the summer. The female buries herself, secretes a sticky fluid from her salivary glands and mixes this with small pieces of soil. From these little bits of paste she makes a spherical nest, using her jaws and front legs in the work, and deposits sixty to a hundred eggs in it, through a hole in the top. This hole is then sealed with more moistened earth and the nest or cocoon is abandoned. The eggs hatch in about a fortnight. The emerging nymphs have at first but three pairs of legs.

Among the groups of insects not included in the foregoing chapters are the Grasshoppers and the Fleas, which suffer only from the disadvantage that they cannot so readily as others be kept in captivity. Grasshoppers form a family of Orthoptera related to the cockroaches. Eleven species belonging to seven genera are found in Britain, and are described in Dr. Malcolm Burr's book. They are insects that are well worth studying, partly because of their relation to the terrible Locust, and partly because our knowledge of their distribution in this country is very incomplete.

Fleas are a group, the order Siphonaptera, of which forty-six species are British. Among these most people are concerned only with one, *Pulex irritans*, but the study of Fleas is a study of a highly specialised order of insects, secondarily wingless and of unusual shape. Moreover, Miriam Rothschild's recent and wonderfully enjoyable book *Fleas, Flukes and Cuckoos* has shown how extremely fascinating a study of these parasites can be.

Groups comparable to these are the Bees and Wasps. The naturalist who has not given insects any particular amount of attention is inclined to think on the one hand of the humble-bee and hive-bee, on the other of the "common wasp" and the hornet, and to retain the impression of two kinds of Bees and two kinds of Wasps. In fact there are about two hundred British Bees and nearly as many Wasps, and all of them deserve attention. For example, the habits of the so-called cuckoo-bees, which lay their eggs in the nests of other Bees, are an excellent subject for study, as are those of the solitary Wasps which provision their cells with paralysed spiders and caterpillars. The activities of these insects provide examples of invertebrate instincts, which are still fertile subjects for discussion and discovery.

These are large groups of insects, each containing several families, and a would-be specialist might begin by choosing one or two families from the group. A more practicable instance of such limitation exists in the Lepidoptera. There are over two thousand British Lepidoptera, fifty-eight of which are Butterflies. By tradition a lepidopterist always collects both Butterflies and moths, yet there seems to be no reason why this should be so. Moreover, they are all of a reasonable size, in contrast to the moths, many of which are so small that only the most enthusiastic have the patience to worry about them. Clearly, an entomologist who decided to limit himself to our five dozen Rhopalocera would find plenty to do apart from filling a few cork-lined boxes with set specimens of the adults. The eggs of Butterflies are often elaborately sculptured and are attractive objects under the microscope, yet few collectors think of examining, drawing and comparing them. The wings of Butterflies are covered with scales, but the scales are not all alike and again they are objects which can form the basis of an interesting set of slides. The elementary text-book tells us that Butterflies have two antennae and a long coiled proboscis, but the antennae are not absolutely uniform, and of the probosces some are very long and some are not so long. There is in all groups of animals a variation in the same character which will always provide a subject for special study.

It is scarcely necessary to point out that the breeding of Butterflies is another side to their study, as also are their general behaviour and their almost mysterious methods of sex-attraction.

Lastly, it is clear that something should be said about the fact that a high proportion of the groups mentioned both in this chapter and elsewhere belong to the class of Insecta. This is inevitable, since among small animals insects are supreme in numbers, in ubiquity and in importance. Therefore the idea arises of making a broad survey of the whole class, adapting some of the principles suggested in the first part of this book to the wider purpose.

The idea is one that can be profitably recommended to any serious biologist, but especially to one who intends later to read zoology at a University or who appreciates the opportunities offered by entomology as the basis of a career.

The course to be taken is the acquisition of a representative of each important order in the great class. As there are only about twenty of these orders, this does not constitute a very difficult task. But its value lies in its variety and its elasticity.

Its variety is due to the diversity of insect form and structure, so that a "type-collection" of insects contains some spirit-specimens, some pinned and set specimens and some mounted as microscopic objects. Thus the making of the collection would take the entomologist over the whole range of preservative methods.

Its elasticity is due to the ease with which the depth of the study can be altered at will, according to the wishes of the collector. Instead of representing an order by a few specimens of one species, it may be decided to include each sub-order, and perhaps in some cases a few of the more important families. The point is that the size of the collection and the scope of the study can be adapted to any scale. At any stage the scale can be enlarged and at all times the whole collection grows towards a systematic demonstration of the nature of the insect world. I have known young biologists embark on this project on several occasions, and always their results have been rewarding. It is undeniably the exact antithesis of the principle of small-group-specialisation on which this book is founded, but it is a plan which appeals to many and has the advantages which always pertain to breadth of view.

Appendix i

THE RELATIONS BETWEEN NATURAL HISTORY
AND BIOLOGY

THERE has long been a general agreement that Biology should form a part of any course in elementary Science, and therefore the teaching of Biology is an accepted portion of the work of many masters and mistresses in many primary and secondary schools. This is of course in addition to Biology of a slightly less elementary kind, which is firmly established as a subject for future students of agriculture, forestry, dentistry or medicine.

One result of this has been the output of a very large number of text-books of Biology, each of which has expressed its writer's contribution to the solving of the problem of how the subject may best be taught; and each in consequence contains some proportion of original thought, a product of its writer's own experience. A study of these books shows that they nearly all lay emphasis, in their prefaces, on the same two points. They have, they say, stressed throughout the essential unity of life; and this, or some such phrase, appears to mean that they have abandoned the simple and satisfying course of dividing the subject into its two components, zoology and botany. Secondly, they say that they have emphasised the desirability of studying the living organism or that they have tried to show the importance of field-work as an adjunct to dissections and laboratory work.

It would be unkind to pursue here the question as to how far these authors are successful in attaining their two desirable but extraordinarily elusive ideals. Every teacher of Biology knows perfectly well that a jumble of chapters which pass from human digestion to photosynthesis and from cockroaches to crocus corms does not really impress on his pupils the idea that all life-processes are essentially similar—if indeed they are. But with this theoretical aspect of Biology teaching this book has not been concerned.

Further, every teacher of Biology knows equally well that field-work and the study-of-the-living-animal are not, save in exceptional instances, possible during the official hours of science teaching that form a part of the school time-table. We all soon discover that the proper time for such work is the half-holiday afternoon and that the proper atmosphere in which it should be done is that of the school Natural History Society or Naturalists' Club.

With the firm establishment of Biology in the schools' curricula the status of the Natural History Society conspicuously improved. Time was when it served only to occupy a few enthusiasts and to employ a few unfortunates who found cricket to be intolerable, together with a proportion of bogus members whose numbers depended on the conditions of membership. All this has now changed in most schools; in others it is changing or will change. This book has been intended in part to appeal to these revivified and enlightened societies.

Recruits to a school Natural History Society are caught young. Many boys arrive each year at a Public School with an interest in Natural History already awakened; often they are ardent collectors of butterflies and moths, or of birds' eggs, or sometimes of beetles. Our first duty is to prevent them from losing their keenness, to convince them that Natural History is a pursuit they may be advised to continue, and at the same time to discourage the possible idea that it is now beneath their dignities as Public Schoolboys to retain an interest in the occupations of their (so distant) past of three or six months ago!

I have tried to suggest one way in which this may be attempted, by developing the instinct of collecting into a further investigation of the animals caught, and by outlining the possibilities that lie in a specialist investigation of a small group of animals about which, all too often, very little is known.

There is, in addition, a most important way in which work of this kind supplements the teaching of biology. The teaching in the school biological laboratory is conditioned by the syllabuses of the public examinations, from the "Ordinary Level" to the First M.B. This may be regrettable, or it may not, but it is a fact; it is also responsible for the dominance of the laboratory corpse over the living animal.

Perhaps we persuade our boys to dig up their own earthworms, but thereafter we *buy* them cockroaches from the Zoo, formalined dogfish from Plymouth, embalmed rats from Manchester, and so on. Many of the animals about which we lecture are unlikely to be seen by our pupils except as stained and mounted microscope slides—beautiful products of someone else's technical skill. It is impossible for them to see the day-to-day life of a dogfish, a fact which justifies the otherwise inexplicable tradition that a biological laboratory must contain an aquarium of guppies or sticklebacks.

It is granted that a biology course could not be derived from the animals included in this book: but these animals are readily obtainable, and they can be studied alive as well as dead. It is undoubtedly true that a boy who has thus investigated the centipedes or the woodlice of his neighbourhood has a far better chance of visualising his pickled crayfish as a living, striving organism.

GLOSSARY

Abdomen—the hindmost portion of an arthropod's body.

Antenna—first of the paired head appendages, usually long, mobile and sensitive.

Apophysis—a projection, outgrowth or branching process.

Cephalothorax—the forepart of the body of a crustacean or an arachnid.

Chitin—a nitrogenous compound of which the exo-skeleton of arthropods is made.

Clypeus—the space between eyes and bases of maxillae.

Coxa—the short segment of a leg, attaching it to the body.

Crop—part of gut in which food is temporarily stored before entering the gizzard.

Ecdysis—moulting, or casting the exo-skeleton in growth.

Elytron—wing of the first pair, modified and hardened to protect the wing behind it.

Femur—the third segment of an arthropod's leg.

Genus—a group of closely related species.

Gizzard—part of gut in which food is broken up before digestion.

Halteres—modified hind wings acting as stabilisers.

Hermaphrodite—male and female sexes in one individual.

Imago—the adult form of an insect.

Instar—the interval between two ecdyses.

Labium—the joined second maxillae or "lower lip."

Labrum—the "upper lip."

Larva—immature form different from the adult and concerned with feeding or dispersal or both.

Mandible—one of the paired mouth-parts; often crushes or bites the food.

Maxilla—the paired mouth-parts behind the mandibles.

Maxillule—the first of two pairs of maxillae in the Crustacea.

Metamorphosis—sudden change of form as from larva to pupa or pupa to imago.

Metatarsus—the penultimate segment of a leg, before the tarsus.

Nymph—immature form similar to the adult except for sex organs.

Ocellus—a simple eye with a single smooth lens-surface.

Palpus—leg-like tactile organ near the mouth of an arthropod.

Pedicel—a narrow "waist" joining abdomen to thorax.

Phylum—the largest subdivision of the animal kingdom.

Pupa—a resting stage between a larva and an imago.
Seta—a hair-like sensory structure on the exo-skeleton of an arthropod.
Spiracle—external opening of a tracheal tube, also called a stigma.
Sternite—a band of chitin across the lower side of a body-segment.
Tarsus—the last, distal segment of an arthropod's limb; usually has several joints.
Tergite—a band of chitin across the upper side of a body-segment.
Thorax—the three leg-bearing segments behind the head.
Tibia—the fourth segment of an arthropodan leg.
Tissue—a group of cells with the same function.
Trachea—an air-carrying tube in the body of an insect.
Trochanter—the second segment of an arthropodan leg.
Xylol—o homologue of benzene, $C_6H_4(CH_3)_2$.

INDEX OF NAMES OF FAMILIES, ORDERS AND CLASSES

INDEX

The page numbers in bold type refer to illustrations

TABLE OF CASES

TABLE OF CASES

TABLE OF CASES

TABLE OF CASES

TABLE OF CASES

INDEX OF NAMES

INDEX OF NAMES

INDEX OF NAMES

INDEX OF NAMES

INDEX TO INTERNATIONAL CONVENTIONS AND TREATIES CITED

INDEX TO INTERNATIONAL CONVENTIONS AND TREATIES CITED

INDEX TO INTERNATIONAL CONVENTIONS AND TREATIES CITED